TEACHING
SCIENCE
to English Learners

STEPHEN FLEENOR

TINA BEENE

Published by Seidlitz Education
P.O. Box 166827
Irving, TX 75016
www.seidlitzeducation.com

For related titles and support materials visit www.seidlitzeducation.com.

4.20

CONTENTS

CHAPTER 1: INTRODUCTION **3**

**CHAPTER 2: THE FUNDAMENTALS OF
TEACHING SCIENCE TO ELS** **7**

ELs in Science | Questioning in Science | The Language of Science

CHAPTER 3: SETTING THE STAGE **15**

Warm-Ups

Uncover the Picture 17

Language Anticipation Guide 18

Visual-Description Matchup 20

Building Background

Vocab Breakdown 23

Gearing up for the Guiding Question 24

Caption the Comic 26

CHAPTER 4: CONTENT DELIVERY **27**

Interactive Lecture

QSSSA 29

Complete the Picture 30

Questioning Conversation .31

Academic Reading

Visual Pre-Read 34

Three Reads, Three Questions 35

"Gimme Five" Summarization Strategy 36

CHAPTER 5: SHOW WHAT YOU KNOW **37**

Academic Writing

Tales from a Graph 39

Example/Non-Example 40

Written Conversation 42

Academic Conversation

Tap and Talk 44

WIT Questioning 45

Expert/Novice 46

CHAPTER 6: ASSESSMENT **47**

Evidence-Based Reasoning

What to do Instead of a Section Review

Vocab Connection Web 53

What I Know/What I Wonder 53

Student Teaching Stations 54

Accommodated Tests

Language Proficiency Differentiation Guide 57

Appendices (I-V) 64

Sources 76

CHAPTER 1
Introduction

From Tina Beene, creator of
Teaching to ELs series

A couple of years ago, over breakfast in a kitschy neighborhood diner— the kind of place with wood paneling and family photos, with almost exclusively regular customers with usual orders — John Seidlitz posed a question to me, and my answer turned into the book you are holding today. He asked me where I would focus my attention if I could tackle just one challenge facing public education. I am pretty sure I started talking about reducing the dropout rate for English learners before he even finished the question. By the time I stepped off my soapbox, my coffee was cold and John was talking me out of starting a revolution. While he admired my passion, he wisely advised that we start with something a little more practical. What could we do, we wondered, that might support teachers in delivering academic content and vocabulary so that English learners (and indeed, all students) would feel more successful and optimistic about their educational prospects?

By the end of the meal, we realized that all I really wanted was to make it a little easier for teachers to embed interactive learning strategies and linguistic supports into their lessons. I wanted to offer professional development that was designed not only around the ways in which instruction is typically delivered but for the way language is used within a particular content area. And I wanted to offer that guidance and those opportunities in the most user-friendly way possible, requiring minimal outside resources and utilizing the best practices in language acquisition that maximize subject-area literacy for all learners.

All of that became all of this and more: a series of books on teaching English learners, with a separate edition for each content area. I felt comfortable tackling *Teaching Social Studies to ELLs* myself because I had experience with the content, so we started there. That project has become one of the most rewarding experiences of my life, and I cannot wait to see what this edition brings. Of course, I knew better than to try and write this one alone. Science teachers can spot flawed methods and overconfidence masking ineptitude more quickly than most; there was no way I would try to pose as an expert when it was not warranted.

We knew that in order to provide the best resource possible, we should follow the guidance of an actual secondary science teacher — a content-area expert with just the right skill set, who could also deliver compelling professional development. It was a tall order, but we kept our eyes and ears open, scouring the state (and beyond) in pursuit of just the right fit. When we met Dr. Stephen Fleenor, we knew he was the scientist we had been seeking. This resource is a reflection of both his brain for science and his heart for kids, and it was my pleasure to bring it to life alongside him.

From Dr. Stephen Fleenor

My plan never was to teach science. My plan was to do science: don a white coat, holster a micropipette, and change the world. The idea came to me in high school, when I learned about scientists genetically engineering sweet potato crops to repel weeds, which saved South African farmers from hours of backbreaking work every day. From that day on, I dove into science head first. Like most kids, however, my problem was visualization: how in the world was this fourteen-year-old, who had barely learned that the mitochondria is the powerhouse of the cell, going to end up a world-leading scientist? Was there some kind of scientist school I could attend? Was there a government agency of elite scientist change agents in which to apply? I had no idea.

Fortunately, I worked in a genetics lab during college, and the professor in charge advised me to go for my Ph.D. Up to that moment, I never would have imagined earning a Ph.D. I had wanted to be a scientist, but I'd never thought I'd be a scientist with a doctorate. I would have considered myself lucky to get into any program, but my professor encouraged me to apply to all of the top-ten Ph.D. programs. I thought she was insane, but she was convinced.

Four years later, I received my Ph.D. from the University of Oxford. In those four years, I performed experiments in a developmental neurobiology lab every day. Yes, I was donning the white coat and, of course, holstering the micropipette. And I loved every minute of it: the new discoveries, however small, that came out of each experiment; the intricacies of interpreting data; and especially the endless coffee and donuts at the departmental seminars. Every day I saw the majesty and wonder of the natural world first-hand, and I was inspired to spread my passion for science to the next generation. So, I began teaching high school science and have been in love with the profession ever since.

There were, admittedly, some hiccups in the plan. I finished the Ph.D. in July, which meant I had to do an emergency three-week certification, and the first day of school was my first day in a high school classroom since my senior year. Needless to say, I struggled to keep my head above water. I was mostly just shocked that the kids weren't falling in love with the subject as easily as I had. Why weren't they understanding the content? Wasn't this the coolest thing they'd ever heard about? I loved my students, and I was eager to create connections to the content for them, so I welcomed any opportunity for professional development. Memorial High School in Edgewood ISD (where I was teaching) is a Title I school in San Antonio, Texas, where 20 percent of the students are English learners. I quickly learned that many of the students who were not labeled "English learners" still struggled with comprehending academic language, in particular the language of science.

> "Teaching science is like telling the most interesting story in the world, but speaking in a foreign and abstract language."

Luckily, my first major professional development experience was in sheltered instruction, and I began applying the principles of language-rich instruction to my science class. At first, admittedly, I was a little skeptical, but as soon as I began implementing the new strategies, I was astounded at the results. Seemingly overnight, I began to hear my students' speaking skills improve to include science vocabulary, to see their writing become more structured around prediction and justifications, and (most importantly) to see their interest in the content increasing dramatically. What's more, my ELs were more engaged and empowered in the lesson than ever. It's like a light bulb went on in every student's mind as, one by one, they realized how cool science is.

Science is a cool subject — it's a really, really cool subject — and it doesn't take much to sell that. The real challenge, I've learned, is increasing students' confidence and aptitude to engage with the complexities of the content. Teaching science is like telling the most interesting story in the world, but speaking in a foreign and abstract language. Of course anyone would love to hear the story, but they would shut down if the words were all gibberish. Learning the language of science, therefore, is the key to unlocking the majesty and wonder of this beautiful subject.

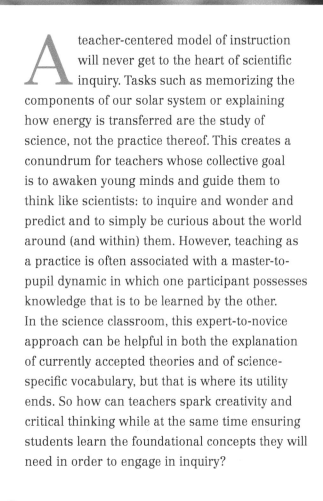

CHAPTER 2
The Fundamentals of Teaching Science to ELs

A teacher-centered model of instruction will never get to the heart of scientific inquiry. Tasks such as memorizing the components of our solar system or explaining how energy is transferred are the study of science, not the practice thereof. This creates a conundrum for teachers whose collective goal is to awaken young minds and guide them to think like scientists: to inquire and wonder and predict and to simply be curious about the world around (and within) them. However, teaching as a practice is often associated with a master-to-pupil dynamic in which one participant possesses knowledge that is to be learned by the other. In the science classroom, this expert-to-novice approach can be helpful in both the explanation of currently accepted theories and of science-specific vocabulary, but that is where its utility ends. So how can teachers spark creativity and critical thinking while at the same time ensuring students learn the foundational concepts they will need in order to engage in inquiry?

For their part, students must understand both the content and the content-specific vocabulary that accompanies it. In order for that to happen, teachers must utilize strategies for making the content comprehensible and the vocabulary memorable. As a result of how the brain processes information, bell-to-bell lecture with little to no visual support will result in minimal curiosity about even the most interesting topics and even less retention of the material.

ENGLISH LEARNERS IN SCIENCE

The challenges posed by science instruction differ somewhat from those faced in the other content areas in terms of scope and scale; both the academic content and the language used to explore it pose identical challenges for ELs and native English speakers alike. Each science course introduces hundreds of new vocabulary words, concepts are often abstract and more often microscopic, and content builds on itself such that a poor or incomplete understanding of fundamental ideas at the beginning of the year may impede deep understanding months down the line. Furthermore, effectively dissecting scientific charts, graphs, and diagrams (an essential part of learning science) requires advanced literacy and inferencing skills that are often underdeveloped both in ELs and in native English speakers.

The good news is that teachers who take the time to embed support for ELs into their lessons facilitate increased content comprehension and vocabulary retention for all students. The strategies that best foster language acquisition provide the same benefits when applied to the "foreign language" of science. By delivering instruction through methods explicitly designed to increase engagement, retention, and communication skills, science teachers everywhere can achieve the seemingly impossible — get students to learn required content without boring them to death in the process — without sacrificing creativity or critical thinking.

This resource is designed to help teachers do exactly that. The chapters are organized around the components of a typical science lesson (such as warm-up, direct teach, or assessment), and each contains three strategies designed to promote engagement and achievement for all students. These strategies are accompanied by appropriate linguistic accommodations for each proficiency level that will help teachers ensure their supports are appropriately challenging for all levels of language learners present.

QUESTIONING IN SCIENCE

For students in the science classroom, asking a question can be a challenging and daunting task; consequently, student questions are uncommon. Asking "Are there any questions?" following a lecture is an almost-guaranteed way to inspire zero questions, except for the one that is loathed by all generations of teachers: "Can I go to the bathroom?" Part of the problem is that asking questions about recently learned content requires deep metacognitive thinking about a student's own previous understanding and how the new information fits into it — a practice in which many students are not well trained. Additionally, from students' perspectives, asking questions is often seen as a weakness, as if a student who did not fully understand a concept the first time it was explained is somehow deficient.

> Question-asking is as fundamental to science as grammar is to language arts or computation is to mathematics.

Still, question-asking is as fundamental to science as grammar is to language arts or computation is to mathematics. Questions drive the scientific process at all stages, and the ability to ask rich, deep questions is essential for scientific thinking. Thus, creating a culture of question-asking in the science classroom generates a culture of deep and rich scientific learning.

Questioning in the Scientific Method

As the endocrinologist Fuller Albright wrote at the conclusion of one of his publications, "I hope I raised more questions than I have given answers" (Manring and Calhoun, 2011, p. 2093). In writing this, Albright appreciated that his greater contribution to

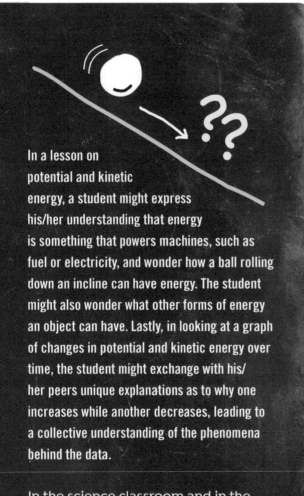

In a lesson on potential and kinetic energy, a student might express his/her understanding that energy is something that powers machines, such as fuel or electricity, and wonder how a ball rolling down an incline can have energy. The student might also wonder what other forms of energy an object can have. Lastly, in looking at a graph of changes in potential and kinetic energy over time, the student might exchange with his/her peers unique explanations as to why one increases while another decreases, leading to a collective understanding of the phenomena behind the data.

In the science classroom and in the scientific community, asking questions is about understanding what one does not know and needs to learn, as well as normalizing around a collective understanding. A lecture presented to 25 students will result in 25 different interpretations of the content. Similarly, a seminar presented to 100 scientists will result in 100 different interpretations of the content. In both cases, discussions driven by questions about the content lead to a collective understanding about the natural world.

the field was not the experiments he performed, but rather the questioning his analysis stimulated about the natural world, which would lead to dozens more follow-up experiments. The scientific method is often misunderstood as a process that begins with a question and ends with an answer. In actuality, the scientific method is an unending, upward spiral. Uncertainties and gaps in understanding prompt questions which lead to increased knowledge but also prompt more uncertainties, gaps, and the potential for alternative interpretation. Likewise, in the science classroom, it is essential for students to express how their understanding fits or does not fit into the content being discussed, to acknowledge what they have not learned about the topic being discussed, and to discuss different interpretations of what data might mean in the context of their learning as they grow in understanding.

Types of Questions

As humans, we are naturally inquisitive beings. Many students, however, believe that the only way to be inquisitive is to ask eloquent, thought-provoking questions that extend the content. This is reinforced by the fact that the askers of these questions are usually the high-performing, highly engaged students of the class who are also first to raise their hands and volunteer an answer. And so, the majority of students believe that unless the question is a "good" question, it should not be asked.

We can change this perception in our classrooms by simply teaching students the various types of questions they can ask. **"Probing" questions** make connections, seek extra details, or form hypotheses about nature. Probing questions are often seen as difficult to produce because they require deep thinking about the content, and many students do not believe they are capable of asking intelligent, probing questions. They don't realize that these are developed through steps of reasoning that can be modeled and taught. Most of the time, this reasoning all occurs silently in the mind of the person asking the question.

I was once fortunate to have a student express out loud her process of reasoning. This led to an extraordinary probing question. I was teaching types of carbohydrates in biology and had just mentioned that paper is made of carbohydrates when a student interrupted, "Wait, paper is a carbohydrate? And glucose is a carbohydrate too? Isn't glucose what plants make in photosynthesis?" I nodded, and after a few moments in which I could almost hear the gears turning in her mind, she asked, "Is that why paper is made from trees, because they do photosynthesis and make a bunch of carbohydrates?"

While the probing question was the end product, it is important to recognize that she asked three simple questions leading up to the probing question. These questions are considered **"clarifying" questions** because they ask for confirmation of understanding about previously discussed content. Clarifying questions can also solicit re-explanation of an idea, or simply express confusion. Asking the question, "Can you explain that again, please?" or using the stem, "I'm confused because…" is an effective way for students to engage with the content while sounding professional and inquisitive. In my classroom, I had a poster for each of these clarifying questions, and I would encourage students to use them throughout the lesson.

For science classes, questions should drive the lessons. The questions that we as science teachers ask can be either **closed-ended** or **open-ended**. When we're leading the class through a lecture, the questions in the moment are often closed-ended, with a short, distinct response that is usually at the "knowledge" level of Bloom's taxonomy. "How many valence electrons does Oxygen have?" or "What stage of metamorphosis occurs after the larval stage?" are both examples of closed-ended questions. There is only one right answer to each question ("six" and "the pupal stage," respectively), and the answer can be provided as quickly as the student can answer it.

Open-ended questions are much more difficult to ask in the spur of the moment, yet they are still an essential component of any lesson plan. Open-ended questions have many right answers in many different formats, and they are at a higher level of Bloom's taxonomy than "knowledge" level questions. For example: "Why does Oxygen form bonds with two Hydrogen atoms in the water molecule?" or "How does a larva change when it enters the pupal stage?" are both examples of open-ended questions. Open-ended questions are particularly effective when students are able to discuss their thoughts in small groups before sharing with the class, such as in the QSSSA protocol outlined on page 29.

Open-ended questions are of utmost importance in a rigorous lesson, but they can be much more difficult to ask than closed-ended questions. We sometimes avoid asking open-ended questions because we don't know how students are going to respond, and we have trouble forming and framing open-ended questions that elicit thoughtful responses and promote further inquiry. For support in converting a closed-ended question into an open-ended question, see Appendix II (p. 66).

The Power of Questioning

Some students enter the school year with highly developed metacognitive skills, ready to ask deep, probing questions. Other students are new to scientific questioning and deep thinking about the content, and they could use support in structuring their thinking. For all students, a culture of question-asking in the science classroom empowers learners to take ownership of their learning. Structures to support students asking questions are infused throughout the activities of this book, e.g., *Uncover the Picture* (p. 17), *Questioning Conversation* (p. 31), and *WIT Questioning* (p. 45).

THE LANGUAGE OF SCIENCE

By its very nature, the language of science poses challenges for students. The sheer volume of terms to be learned in each course is enough to leave students feeling as though they are trying to drink from a firehose. Add to that the fact that the terms (with which they are universally unfamiliar) accumulate, and it is no wonder that teachers and students both become frustrated. The good news is that there are strategies that help students comprehend and manage the massive amounts of vocabulary required in any of the sciences. Strategies that are most effective are often those that most benefit English learners. EL-focused practices provide a kind of "rising tide raises all boats" effect, leading all students to better understand terms, concepts, and the world around them.

Vocabulary

CHALLENGES: The vocabulary of science poses significant challenges for students. Concepts are often explained in a hierarchical fashion, beginning with one aspect or term and then building from that point. The initial point of reference might move from the "whole" to its "parts," or understanding might expand from the smallest detail to the big idea. Understanding the nature of a molecule, for example, depends on understanding the nature of atoms. If meaning breaks down for students at any point in this process, the chain of understanding will be severed. At that point, the best-case scenario is that comprehension will deteriorate only slightly, leading to a few misconceptions and false conclusions. More likely, however, the student will become frustrated, confused, or both, to such an extent that understanding will break down completely and vocabulary acquisition will cease. Thus it is essential that lessons provide opportunities for students to strengthen background knowledge. In Chapter 3 (p. 15), we provide specific activities for building background.

GIFTS: The prevalence of Greek and Latin roots (see Appendix III) in science vocabulary provides numerous cognates that can be helpful for many English learners (see Appendix IV) as they may find connections to their own language. Both English learners and native speakers of English benefit from acquiring increasing familiarity with Greek and Latin roots because it expands their knowledge of both the English language and scientific concepts.

Structure

CHALLENGES: The language of science differs from that of other content areas in both format and intent. While language arts and history often utilize a narrative format to describe social relationships and events, science is more concerned with technical descriptions of the natural world and its processes. This "just the facts, ma'am" approach can be confusing to students who attempt to make sense of their reading through application of strategies learned in language arts or history to their science text.

As a scientist, my own story is a case study in not being explicitly taught scientific writing. The fact that I did not know how to write scientifically first came to light in college, when I began writing laboratory reports. "Flowery," "get to the point," and "why

do I care what you believe?" were common themes inscribed in the margins in blood-red ink. After having received endless praise from high school English teachers for my writing aptitude, I felt completely shot down by the criticisms coming in my college science classes. Concise, third person, and passive voice might as well have been words of a foreign language. As a result, I found myself lacking confidence in class. I developed into an apt scientific writer only after years of receiving and responding to specific feedback. I always wished that I had been taught explicitly and given opportunities to write scientifically in my high school science classes. It was not until many years later, when I finished the first draft of my Ph.D. thesis, that I truly regained the confidence I once had in my high school English classes. A single comment was written on the last page, in the same shade of red: "Well put."

GIFTS: Written with a third-person, passive voice, science texts are — quite frankly — boring. However, as I began to understand from my own development as a scientific writer, there are many advantages inherent in the structure of scientific writing. The objectivity of science texts makes for predictable, unambiguous structures. A laboratory report, for example, is simply the sequence of hypothesis, procedures, results, and conclusion, with background knowledge and analysis gluing the report together as justification (see Chapter 6, p. 47). This is the invariable structure of a laboratory report; with a few thinking stems, writing it is simply filling in the gaps.

Additionally, science texts are anchored by rich visuals such as graphs, tables, diagrams, micrographs, and flow charts. Analysis of scientific texts, therefore, activates diverse modalities of thinking, and while the text itself is often formulaic, the visual presentation of data or models allows for varied demonstrations of learning. A geological text, for example, is suddenly much less boring when it includes a rich diagram that synthesizes knowledge about the stages of sedimentation. Scientific language structures scientific thinking. As I once stated in a blog post:

> ❝ *The shift towards teaching science as a language essentially depends on a mind-shift about what students need to learn. The standards are densely packed with science content which teachers understandably often feel compelled to deliver as quickly as possible. But when students are taught the process of constructing science, the content comes fluidly and efficiently. Ultimately, teaching the language of science not only dramatically helps ELs acquire English, but also forms all students into thinking and acting scientists.* ❞

CHAPTER 3
Setting the Stage

✔ Warm-Ups

✔ Building Background

By its nature, the acquisition of scientific knowledge is cumulative, meaning that new learning is built on the foundation of previous knowledge. This explains why technological innovation has progressed so exponentially over the course of human history. Every time scientists sit down to craft hypotheses or plan new experiments, they draw upon centuries of human learning and years of their own experiences. In the words of Sir Isaac Newton, great scientific discoveries are made "standing on the shoulders of giants."

The cumulative nature of scientific knowledge makes it imperative to set the stage for every lesson so that students can acquire new learning based on prior knowledge. In all learning environments, however, students enter with different degrees of prior knowledge, and introducing the lesson in a way that engages and prepares all students is challenging. Compounding this challenge are the diverse levels of English language proficiency that ELs bring to the classroom.

In this chapter, we address these challenges with strategies that set the stage by tapping into individual students' prior knowledge and activating students' deep thinking about the new core ideas of the lesson. All of the strategies presented require minimal amounts of prep time and provide an approach to successfully engaging students while introducing new content. Alongside these strategies, we've suggested linguistic accommodations for differentiating instruction by language proficiency level. These accommodations should be viewed as descriptive rather than prescriptive; in some instances, certain students may need scaffolded supports that exceed what has been suggested, whereas in other tasks, fewer supports may be necessary. The success of these evolving accomodations is predicated on a classroom environment in which students feel comfortable requesting and utilizing linguistic supports. Once their language needs have been taken into account, the stage is set for students to enter into the lesson and begin listening, reading, speaking, and writing like scientists.

WARM-UPS

Beginning each class with a warm-up or bellringer offers several benefits. It creates a consistent structure or routine, which puts students at ease and makes it easier for them to internalize the content to be shared that day. It also engages them with the overall objective of the day while priming their brains to take in new information. It can offer all students an opportunity to experience academic success, which encourages them to put forth more effort throughout the rest of the lesson, and it also offers one more avenue for building vocabulary through listening, speaking, reading, and/or writing.

Uncover the Picture

The teacher projects an image to the class that is partially covered. The image is slowly uncovered while students list things they see. The teacher pauses three times to let students make predictions about the image.

What do you notice?

Where/how was this photograph taken?

(if microscopic) How many times zoomed in do you imagine this photograph was?*

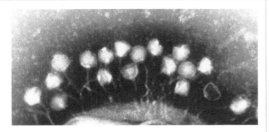

What else do you see in the image now?

What do you think you'll see in the final section of the photograph?

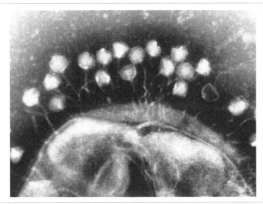

What surprised you about the second and third sections of this photograph?

What questions do you have now that you've seen the entire photograph?

*In life sciences and chemistry, it is highly recommended that photographs taken from microscopes are often used to encourage students to think about the scale of life.

NEWCOMER/BEGINNER	INTERMEDIATE	ADVANCED	NEARLY FLUENT
Students are each provided a copy of the image and are asked to identify components of the image by correctly labeling them with assistance from a word bank. Students may choose to translate terms into their native language. *I see a...*	Teachers give students an appropriate amount of wait time before asking them to identify components of the image and add descriptors. *I noticed a...*	Students could be expected to elaborate on their predictions using more complex grammar structures. *It is significant that ___ because...*	Students identify items/ideas; make predictions. *I'm wondering if ___ because...*

Language Anticipation Guide *(Head & Readence, 1986)*

Students are presented with academic terms and phrases that will be discussed in the day's lesson alongside possible definitions of the terms. Students select whether the stated definition is the true definition in the context of the day's lesson. This is particularly effective to familiarize students with "mortar" words that are not taught explicitly and can have different definitions in non-academic versus academic contexts (for example, a data "table" compared to a dinner "table").

1. Select three to eight key words or phrases in a science-related text.

2. Write a true/false statement for each key word focusing on the meaning of the word as it is used in the passage. This set of statements becomes the Language Anticipation Guide (see facing page).

After instruction, students revisit their initial predictions of what the words meant to see if any need adjustment.

3. Have students examine the statements prior to reading and decide if the statements are true or false. This may be done individually, but it is a great opportunity for paired academic discussion as well.

4. Have students read the passage, taking note of the context surrounding each word from the Language Anticipation Guide.

5. Have students make changes to their true/false choices in light of any new understandings they formed while reading.

6. Conduct a brief, whole-group discussion for each Language Anticipation Guide statement.

STATEMENT	BEFORE READING	AFTER READING
The word *produce* means fruits and vegetables sold at a supermarket.	TRUE | FALSE	TRUE | FALSE
The word *strain* means to struggle.	TRUE | FALSE	TRUE | FALSE
The word *exposure* means for something to come into contact with something else.	TRUE | FALSE	TRUE | FALSE

NEWCOMER/BEGINNER	INTERMEDIATE	ADVANCED	NEARLY FLUENT
Students complete one to two items using a native-language resource for support: *I choose (true/false) for number 1.*	Students complete both Before and After columns with teacher support as needed for non-key terms within the statements. They discuss any adjustments made to "before" predictions using the following stem: *I chose (true/false) for the word ___. Now I think...*	Students complete both Before and After columns with minimal assistance. They discuss any adjustments made to "before" predictions using this stem: *At first I thought number ___ was (true / false) but now I think ____ because...*	Students complete both Before and After columns without assistance. They discuss any adjustments made to "before" predictions after reading using the following stem: *After reading, I changed my answer on number ___ to (true/false) based on...*

Visual–Description Matchup

Designed to help students connect visuals to new vocabulary terms, this strategy increases comprehension while fostering relationships among students through interaction and movement.

1. Students receive cards with either a visual or a description of one of the lesson's vocabulary words.

2. Students walk around the room and find another person who has a complementary card (a description that matches the visual or vice versa).

3. Students discuss why they believe their visual depicts the description or why the description matches the visual.

4. The teacher then conducts a whole-group discussion showing the students the correct visual-description matchup as well as which vocabulary word correctly matches each description.

NEWCOMER/BEGINNER	INTERMEDIATE	ADVANCED	NEARLY FLUENT
Students may locate their partners more easily if they are provided the visual portion of the pairing.	After clarification of pronunciation of key terms, students complete this activity without further accommodation, though errors in verbal communication are to be expected.	Advanced students need the opportunity to practice new content-area vocabulary, so their stems should be designed to promote academic language use.	Nearly fluent students benefit from multiple opportunities to practice new vocabulary with a native-speaking partner when possible. Their stems should be designed to elicit more complex grammar and additional detail.
My card shows (a/the).... *Your card shows (a/the)....*	*My card shows (a/the) ____. It matches the word...*	*I think our cards match because...* *They might be associated with the term...*	*I think our cards match because...* *They are associated with the term ____ because...*

BUILDING BACKGROUND

Arguably the most important part of the scientific method is forming a hypothesis. This is when scientists forge connections between the disparate pieces of background knowledge they have in order to make a prediction. In order to mirror the scientific process, an introduction to a science lesson will frequently include hypothesizing about new learning in addition to recollecting prior knowledge. This establishes a context within which students can frame their thinking about new content.

Take, for example, the process of cellular respiration in which glucose is metabolized to produce usable energy for cells, releasing carbon dioxide as a by-product. Imagine starting with the question, "How do you lose weight?" This is a question all students have thought or heard about at least some point in their lives, so it is accessible to everyone. "Exercise" is an expected response. The teacher could then drive the class to think about cellular respiration through his/her questioning:

Teacher: Okay, exercise helps you lose weight. But how do you physically lose mass from your body?

Cynthia: You lose weight by sweating.

Teacher: You definitely lose a lot of water when you sweat (wipes hand across forehead). But don't you gain it right back when you drink more water? How does mass leave your body?

Thomas: When you go to the bathroom?

Teacher: You're right, you lose mass when you go to the bathroom. But do you go to the bathroom more when you lose weight? How else does mass leave your body?

Yesennia: When you breathe out, gas leaves your body.

Teacher: And that gas has mass that is exhaled when you breathe out. What is in that gas?

Jorge: The gas is carbon dioxide (points to board).

Teacher: Carbon dioxide (exhales visibly while pointing to mouth). You're right, the gas you exhale is (emphasizes) carbon dioxide. But where does the (emphasizes) carbon in the carbon dioxide come from?

Maria: Didn't you say last week that all organisms are made of carbon? So is the fat on your body made of carbon?

Teacher: That's exactly right! So if exercise "burns fat," then the carbon in your fat must be released into your lungs as carbon dioxide. But where does the fat come from?

David: Fat comes from eating too much food.

Teacher: Good, David. And where did that food come from?

David: Plants, or the animals that ate plants.

Teacher: So plants make food for us, and that food is made of carbon. Where did those plants get the carbon from to make the food?

Jorge: Plants make food from the carbon dioxide you breathe out!

In this approach, different levels of background knowledge were brought up, and the students were able to make connections between disparate facts. In fact, so many connections were made that direct teaching of the details of the process of cellular respiration will be like icing on the cake of students' conceptual understanding. Not to mention, it was engaging. Students' natural predictive curiosity was engaged because they were questioning the natural world with which they're already intimately familiar.

Building background is especially important for ELs, who might not realize they have prior knowledge about a subject because the new learning is in English. It is important to note that effective background building cannot only be accessible to fluent listeners; robust supports such as hand gestures, visuals, emphasized vocabulary, and sentence stems are necessary to engage all students. In the example on pg. 21, the teacher made deliberate hand gestures and emphasized vocabulary words. Also, the vocabulary words were clearly already introduced to the students. It is especially important in science that pronunciation of vocabulary words is modeled at the start of the lesson by slowly repeating syllables to build up to each word (for example, "*thy-, thy-, thy-la, thy-la, thy-la-koid, thylakoid*").

The activities in this section engage students in predictive thinking connected to vocabulary and recommend specific supports to help reach all learners.

Vocab Breakdown

The teacher breaks the vocabulary words into prefixes, roots, and suffixes and assigns the parts of a vocabulary word to each member of a group. The teacher also provides the students with the meaning of each prefix, suffix, and root. Students are given two to three minutes to draw a picture to represent each word part. Students should be encouraged to think of other words that also use each part, such as "unicorn" using "uni" or "nucleus" using "nuc." Then students are instructed to present their pictures in their groups, describing what they think each whole vocabulary word means.

Example: Endosymbiotic *(describing a cooperative relationship of bacteria functioning as organelles inside eukaryotic cells)*

See Appendix III for definitions of prefixes, suffixes, and roots.

NEWCOMER/BEGINNER	INTERMEDIATE	ADVANCED	NEARLY FLUENT
The visual nature of this task minimizes the accommodations necessary for students. They should be allowed to remain silent during the group discussion and should be allowed to utilize a native-language resource to complete the activity.	Students utilize simple sentence stems to participate in the group discussion. Students complete the individual/pair discussion with assistance from a native-language or peer resource as needed. *I drew a _____ because...*	Students should be encouraged to seek clarification of any classmate's answer when needed by using the WIT questioning method (See p. 45). *Why do you think?* *Is there another...?* *Tell me more about...*	Students should be encouraged to construct multiple responses for the same prefix, suffix, etc. where possible.

Gearing Up for the Guiding Question

Students are presented the central question of the lesson (the guiding question) and the key vocabulary of the day, and are instructed to discuss the question with a partner, using the key vocabulary, for three minutes before attempting to answer it. Each vocabulary word should be accompanied by an explanatory, text-minimal visual (see example on facing page) and pronunciation should be modeled as on page 22. An optional "big-picture" visual that represents the crux of the lesson can also drive the discussion. The discussion should be structured around sentence stems such as these:

- *I think the question is asking...*

- *I think the word _____ is important to the question because...*

- *The words _____ and _____ are related by...*

- *I think that the word _____ means...because...*

- *The picture makes me think of...because...*

Students should then be provided a new sentence stem to answer the guiding question and given two to three minutes to write independently, with encouragement to use the vocabulary terms that have just been discussed. This activity is particularly effective if the students are presented the question again as a "closure" at the end of lesson and are required to use all vocabulary words to answer the question in paragraph form.

NEWCOMER/BEGINNER	INTERMEDIATE	ADVANCED	NEARLY FLUENT
During the writing component, students can apply labels to any "big picture" visual that pertains to the lesson and then complete simple sentence stems that reflect the guiding question using a word bank for key vocabulary.	Frequent errors should be expected in conversation and in writing, particularly in terms of verb tense and vague pronouns, due to the speed of the activity. Students may need to use a combination of their native language and English during the paired conversation if their partner comprehends both languages, but should be encouraged to complete the writing in English (using resources such as the word bank for support).	Students should be encouraged to use stems during the conversation that will subsequently enhance their writing when the guiding question is presented again as a closure activity.	Students should be expected to utilize complex sentence stems that encourage abstract thinking and expression during the discussion phase.

Guiding Question:

How does ecological succession affect species diversity?

VOCABULARY

Species

Diversity

Ecological Succession

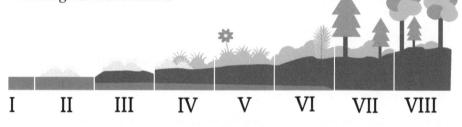

| I | II | III | IV | V | VI | VII | VIII |

time

I think _____ affects

_____because....

Caption the Comic

1. Present students with a series of three to five images in the format of a comic strip (logically sequenced with a cause-and-effect relationship). The images relate to the content of the lesson and can be readily found on web searches. (For natural processes such as sedimentation or transcription, web searches will show images already presented in a sequence.)

2. Instruct the students to write captions in narrative language that describe each image and connect the images together in a story. Sentence stems can help to focus students on sequential and/or the cause-and-effect relationships of the images.

3. Have students write captions for three to five minutes.

4. Have students tell their "stories" in partners or groups.

NEWCOMER/BEGINNER	INTERMEDIATE	ADVANCED	NEARLY FLUENT
Before the lesson, students can be provided native-language resources related to the topic. Students should be permitted to complete their work in their native language.	Before the lesson, students can be provided native-language resources related to the topic. Students should be able to complete this task with minimal support because stems will be provided to all students.	Students benefit from teacher modeling of the use of transitional and sequential language. Students can be expected to perform like non-EL students in this task.	Students can be expected to perform like non-EL students in this task.

CHAPTER 4
Content Delivery

✔ Interactive Lecture

✔ Academic Reading

Once students have primed their minds by thinking deeply about their prior knowledge, they are able to delve into new learning of rich content. This new learning is analogous to the data acquisition step of the scientific method. The idea of "analyzing scientific data" might stir up images of a scientist passively taking readings from a machine in the corner of a laboratory, mindlessly copying information from a screen. On the contrary, data acquisition is actually one of the most cognitively demanding steps of the scientific process, requiring focus and engagement. Picture a scientist observing the formation of a tornado while inferring patterns and analyzing data as it comes out in real time.

Similarly, the new learning that occurs through lectures and reading demands intense focus and deep engagement. This is particularly true for ELs, who have to decipher all of the contextual language in addition to the new content. In this chapter, we describe strategies that are structured to let students take an active role in learning. Implementing these strategies through interactive lecture and structured, academic reading will enable students to engage deeply with the content while also enabling them to maintain the required focus for data retention.

INTERACTIVE LECTURE

We all lecture during instruction. It is unavoidable as we give students directions, demonstrate how to use instructional materials, and outline key concepts. The question is not whether or not to lecture, but how to do it in such a way that we keep our students engaged and focused (especially our English learners). We know that students' minds need time to interact with new information in order to process and store it, so it should not come as a surprise that engaging in bell-to-bell monologues without structured opportunities for students to listen, speak, read, and write results in minimal retention of information. This practice is particularly burdensome for ELs.

Besides taking in the new content, ELs are simultaneously trying to acquire proficiency in English, and they can become so mentally exhausted by non-stop lectures that their brains simply shut down. Imagine trying to watch an hour-long TV show in the foreign language you're trying to learn, without the opportunity to turn on subtitles, pause and reflect, or ask anyone to explain what is going on. It won't be long before you either turn off the program or stop actively listening and just watch the screen hoping to gain any understanding of the plot from the visuals alone. Either way, you won't be acquiring a new language!

In the same way that you would need the subtitles, the pauses, and the explanations to learn the foreign language, students attempting to acquire the "foreign language" of science will need structures that chunk the instructional time and information, make the content and language comprehensible, and allow them time to process the material. This structuring is doubly essential for English learners, as they are acquiring the foreign language of English at the same time. Providing opportunities for the students to actively participate during lectures allows them to interact with and process the new content rather than passively copying notes — a task which might not be possible for students at very low levels of English language proficiency. These structures also provide opportunities for ELs to make sense of the spoken and written language to which they have been exposed.

The following activities can be readily incorporated at the beginning, during, or at the end of any lecture, and can often even be employed multiple times in one lecture.

QSSSA *(Seidlitz & Perryman, 2011)*

This strategy is highly versatile and can be used any time the teacher wants to ask an open-ended* question in a whole-group environment. The teacher presents the question to the class, pausing at the end to give the students time to think. The teacher provides students with a specific response signal to indicate when they are ready to answer and a sentence stem to use for their response. After sharing their responses with partners, students are chosen randomly to share with the whole group.

Question: Ask the class a question.

Signal: Ask students to use a specific response signal when they are ready to answer the question.

Stem: Provide students with a sentence stem to use when answering the question.

Share: Give students an opportunity to share their responses with other students in pairs, triads, or groups.

Assess: Determine the quality of student discussions and the level of understanding by randomly selecting students to share out loud or by having all students write their responses.

Question	Signal	Stem	Share	Assess
How is an element different from a compound?	Pencils/pens down	An element is different from a compound because…	Partners (odd-numbered students go first)	Random selection

NEWCOMER/BEGINNER	INTERMEDIATE	ADVANCED	NEARLY FLUENT
Students should be able to complete the sentence stem *after* working with their partners. They should not be expected to speak in front of the whole group unless they volunteer.	Students should be able to complete the stem before working with partners. The share portion should help them clarify their thinking. They might need to be reminded that the stem is available when sharing with the whole group.	Students are encouraged to use the most complex stem provided or create their own sentence(s).	Students should be expected to use the most complex stem provided or create their own sentence(s).

*For support converting closed-ended questions into open-ended questions, see Appendix II (p. 66).

Complete the Picture

1. A half-covered diagram, picture, or graph is projected or printed out and given to students. The visual should be directly related to the content being taught in the lecture.

2. Students are instructed to complete the second half of the visual to their best estimation.

3. In partners or groups, the students then have a structured conversation about how they completed the drawing and why they completed it the way they did.

4. The teacher then leads a whole-class discussion in which he/she shares the rest of the visual.

Sentence Stems:
I drew...because...
I included...in the other half of the drawing because...

PRESENTED TO STUDENTS	REVEALED DURING DISCUSSION
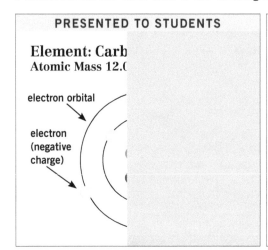	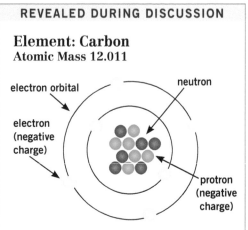

NEWCOMER/BEGINNER	INTERMEDIATE	ADVANCED	NEARLY FLUENT
The visual nature of this task minimizes the accommodations necessary for students, beyond those typically necessary for a structured conversation (See QSSSA). *I drew (a/the) _____.*	Students should be able to complete this task with minimal support because stems will be provided to all students. *I drew _____ because....*	Students can be expected to perform like non-EL students in this task. *In my drawing, I included _____ because...*	Students can be expected to perform like non-EL students in this task.

Questioning Conversation

Questions form the heart of the scientific process. It is impossible to ask a meaningful question about science content without analyzing that content deeply. This activity provides a structure for students to craft their own questions about the content. It is important to ensure the students are instructed not only to ask questions but also to offer their guesses (their *hypotheses*) to the answers.

1. Students individually develop a question using a sentence stem, such as the following:
   - *One thing I don't know is...*
   - *When the teacher talked about ___, it made me wonder...*
   - *I did not understand when the teacher said _____, but I think...*

2. Students then develop hypotheses to answer their own questions.
   - *I think...*
   - *Based on _____ I believe...*
   - *_____ made me think _____ because...*

3. Students conduct a discussion using their questions and hypotheses in partners or groups.

4. The teacher calls on students randomly to share their questions and their hypotheses.

The structure of the provided sentence stems is very deliberate. It is important that students are sharing their questions and hypotheses and not trying to "quiz" each other, as this can create a mental block for students who are not as confident in their understanding of the content. Rather, the sentence stems are designed for students to express and attempt to address their uncertainty. The third sentence stem is designed for struggling learners to reflect metacognitively on their learning. This forms a clarification inquiry which, though not as deep as a probing question, is important for scientists to ask.

NEWCOMER/BEGINNER	INTERMEDIATE	ADVANCED	NEARLY FLUENT
Students should be able to complete the sentence stem after working with their partners. They should not be expected to speak in front of the whole group unless they volunteer.	Students should be able to complete the stem before working with their partners. The share portion should help them clarify their thinking. They might need to be reminded that the stem is available when sharing with the whole group.	Provided they are very familiar and have sufficient background knowledge with the materials, students should be able to engage in these conversations with minimal support. They should be encouraged to seek clarification from the teacher or their partners when needed.	Teacher modeling of the expectations for conversation should be sufficient support for students, who should be reminded to seek clarification as needed.

ACADEMIC READING

It might seem counterintuitive to consider academic reading as a primary means of acquiring new content knowledge. After all, reading academic texts has traditionally been reserved for homework or information-gathering to supplement lectures. And yet, "research continues to show that for students to fully access the science curriculum, it is critical to address effective ways to increase reading comprehension of expository science text" (Kaldenberg et al., 2015, p. 160). But because expository science text is often so dense and vocabulary-laden, students tend to struggle with academic reading in science (Johnson and Zabrucky, 2011). In addition, science texts often contain *polysemic words* (words that have different meanings in different contexts) and even more often employ *nominalized words* (words converted from one part of speech into a noun, e.g., "defor-estation" from the verb 'deforest') (Patterson et al., 2018). Without structured practice in understanding science texts, students face a heavy disadvantage on standardized exams, in future science courses, and when pursuing future careers in STEM fields.

Over the past few decades, science instruction has shifted toward inquiry-based learning, in which students learn by engaging in hands-on activities and asking questions about what they observe. This has raised concern among some educators and educational researchers that inquiry-based learning pushes reading to the wayside; on the contrary, strong academic reading is fundamental to proper inquiry-based learning. This is because the effectiveness of hands-on interaction with natural phenomena depends entirely on students' understanding of the science on which the phenomena are based. To this end, scientists, sociolinguists and experts of science education agree that reading comprehension and literacy is essential for students to be successful scientists (Patterson et al., 2018).

Strong academic reading is fundamental to proper inquiry-based learning. The effectiveness of hands-on interaction with natural phenomena depends entirely on students' understanding of the science on which the phenomena are based.

I, personally, learned this the hard way while doing research for my Ph.D. dissertation. I had to read hundreds of primary scientific research publications. I remember spending hours laboring over the first publication, highlighting information I thought was important and taking notes. The next day, when a colleague asked me about the paper, I was horrified by the fact that I struggled to remember a single word. I realized that though I had developed great reading proficiency over my educational career, I had never learned how to proficiently read scientific texts with comprehension. Thus, in my case, and in the case of all of our future scientists, it is essential that we provide opportunities for our students to develop comprehension skills of scientific texts.

By incorporating structured academic reading into our lessons, our students will gain the skills necessary for comprehending science texts while simultaneously learning new science content. As Nancy Motley explains in *Talk, Read, Talk, Write*, "the text, rather than the lecture, is the manner in which students acquire new content area knowledge" (2016, p. 34). In this section, we present strategies geared specifically toward engaging students with science texts while promoting deep thinking about new science content.

Visual Pre-Read

1. The teacher presents a text (e.g., journal article, textbook passage, abstract, lab report, etc.) with an accompanying visual (diagram, graph, image, etc.).

2. Before reading, students are instructed to analyze the title of the text as well as the visual and make predictions about the content of the text.

3. Students discuss in partners or groups what they notice about the title and visual and what they predict the text will be about. The following sentence stems can be used to facilitate conversation:

   • *I predict this text will be about…because…*

   • *The diagram/graph is related to the title because…*

   • *From the _____, I can tell that _____ will be important to the article because…*

4. The teacher then randomly selects students to share their analyses and predictions with the whole group.

NEWCOMER/BEGINNER	INTERMEDIATE	ADVANCED	NEARLY FLUENT
Teacher models the use of the stems and pronounces the words found in titles, captions, and subtitles. Allow students to use native language/drawing to express comprehension of the visual material.	Teacher models the use of the stems before students discuss the stems with their partners. Speaking with partners should help them clarify their thinking and provide an opportunity for language practice.	Allow students time to rehearse their responses before sharing with the group. They might choose to use their own words instead of the stems.	Students should be encouraged to use a variety of sentence structures and should, after practice, be able to pronounce academic terms correctly.

Three Reads, Three Questions

1. Students are presented with a short (1-3 paragraph) text and instructed to read with the purpose of completing this sentence stem:

   This passage was about...

2. Students discuss their responses in partners or groups, then are instructed to read the passage again. This time, however, the purpose of reading is addressing this stem:

   What the author assumed I knew was...

3. Students discuss their responses just as before, and this time the teacher has representatives from each group share any words or ideas that the author assumed the student knew. The teacher writes the terms on the board and briefly explains what each one means. For example, the teacher writes "synthetic compounds" on the board and explains that these are molecules made in a lab and are not naturally occurring. The teacher then might write "made in lab" next to the term.

4. The students are then instructed to read through the passage one last time with the purpose of discussing this stem:

   What changed my understanding was...

NEWCOMER/BEGINNER	INTERMEDIATE	ADVANCED	NEARLY FLUENT
Provide newcomer students with a translation of the article in their native language (for example, using Google Chrome's translate function). Additionally, provide the students a simple outline of the article in English that contains the key terms. The newcomer student might observe a pair composed of either ELs and/or native English speakers, then complete the writing in his/her native language, with key terms translated into English.	Students should be provided with a graphic organizer or a simple outline of the article in English that contains the key terms. It is helpful for the teacher to pre-teach the vocabulary and pronounce any key terms that the students may struggle with while reading the text.	Students can be provided with a graphic organizer to support comprehension of the text.	Students should be provided with visual supports and modeling of pronunciation if the text is on a topic with which they have very little familiarity.

"Gimme Five" Summarization Strategy

When asked to summarize a given text, students often struggle to relate only the most crucial information. Providing a frame for their summaries gives students instructional scaffolding that naturally narrows their focus onto what the teacher would most like for them to retain. Whatever format is used, students should be given sufficient think time and the opportunity to record their answers before forming partners or groups so that they might better organize their thoughts before sharing.

A "Gimme Five" summary consists of five facts from the reading, counted off on each finger until the entire fist has been shared.

Example:

Teacher: Okay class, we're coming to the end of our time today. We didn't finish this passage, so we'll need to summarize what we've read so far if we want our brains to pick up tomorrow where we left off today. I'd like for you to take a moment to complete a "Gimme Five" summary by yourself. When you're ready to share, please stand up. When you see your noon appointment is also standing, get together and share your thoughts. The younger student will share first. You'll also meet again tomorrow at the beginning of class to review your summaries; that time the older student will start.

Appointment calendars allow for numerous partnerships to be formed without time spent finding new partners. Students are given blank agendas with time slots for each hour, which they fill by setting appointments with classmates as they move around the room. After their appointments have been set, students can be instructed to meet with various partners (2 p.m. partner or 9 a.m. partner, etc.) for a week or two before a new calendar is necessary.

NEWCOMER/BEGINNER	INTERMEDIATE	ADVANCED	NEARLY FLUENT
Students should be provided with an adapted or native-language version of the text before reading the grade-level text in English. Students should highlight two or three facts from either text.	Students can be provided with an adapted text and given time to write down their summaries before sharing.	Students should be provided time to request clarification for unfamiliar terms found within text.	Students should be encouraged to try to select more significant rather than less significant facts in their "Gimme Five" summaries.

CHAPTER 5
Show What You Know

✔ Academic Writing

✔ Academic Conversation

A s teachers, we often think of writing and talking merely as ways for students to "show what they know." However, writing and talking are also ways for students to deepen their comprehension of science concepts and explore new ideas. In this chapter, we provide two approaches for students to demonstrate and solidify their understanding of science: academic writing and academic conversations.

ACADEMIC WRITING

The value of providing students opportunities to express their learning in a structured, formal manner cannot be understated. Writing is particularly important in the conceptually complex, vocabulary-rich environment of the science classroom because it helps students synthesize new ideas and make new connections within the content.

Science writing, however, is challenging for many students because it is dramatically different from the descriptive, narrative, and persuasive formats they are familiar with from their English classes. Students might struggle to write objectively, without expressing their opinions, or have trouble correctly structuring sentences around complex vocabulary (for example, "the cell undergoes mitosis" instead of "the cell has mitosis" or "the cell is mitosis"). These challenges are multiplied for ELs who might also struggle with basic grammar and syntax.

And yet, the structure and formal nature of science writing supports language development for all students. Writing in the language-rich science classroom is found in the forms of journal entries, formal assessments, and exit tickets. Prompts for science writing usually use the following verbs: state/identify/label, compare/contrast, describe, explain, predict, and justify. Science students are also sometimes asked to draw or illustrate and to calculate, but these processes are supplemental to the written product. Examples of science writing verbs aligned with Bloom's Taxonomy (1956) are provided in the table below.

Bloom's Taxonomy	Verb	The student is able to...	Example
knowledge	state/identify/label*	recall facts or match vocabulary to visual	Label the parts of a plant.
comprehension	describe	provide characteristic details about a concept	Describe how the appearance of the moon changes as it rotates around the Earth.
	compare/contrast	categorize characteristic details about multiple concepts	Compare and contrast physical properties of metals and non-metals.
analysis	explain	connect characteristic details of a concept to other concepts	Explain why earthquakes occur frequently in mountainous regions.
evaluation	predict**	understand the effect(s) of untested experiments	Predict the impact on the carbon cycle following a massive forest fire.
	justify	use characteristic details of concepts to explain the results of novel experiments	Justify why the pressure would increase in the chamber following a temperature rise.

* In isolation, "state/identify/label" prompts exist at the knowledge level of Bloom's taxonomy. However, if "state/identify/label" verbs are applied to data tables or graphs, they can be used at the analysis level of Bloom's taxonomy.

** In science writing prompts, "predict" is often paired with "justify."

In this section, we outline three strategies that get students to think critically about the content while providing structures that set students up for clear academic writing.

Tales from a Graph

The teacher presents a labeled graph and asks the students to write one or two paragraphs analyzing the experiment on which the graph was based. Students should be encouraged to write a description of the actions the scientist(s) took in the experiment and the process of experimentation. The "story" should address the following questions:

1. What was measured? How was the data measured?
   _____ *was measured by...*

2. Why did the scientist(s) choose to measure those data?
   The scientist(s) measured those data because...

3. What were the results of the experiment?
   The results of the experiment were...

4. What connection can you make between these results and what we are learning in class?
   This means...

The structure of the provided sentence stems encourages students to write using both passive and active voice. This mixture helps them to transition from the writing style of their English language arts classes to scientific writing.

NEWCOMER/BEGINNER	INTERMEDIATE	ADVANCED	NEARLY FLUENT
Students could be expected to label a graph using labels provided in a word bank and should be able to use the terms in pre-constructed sentence frames. Simplified stems could include the following: *The title of the graph is... The X-axis measures... The Y-axis measures... One thing that changed on the graph is...*	Students should be able to complete this task with minimal support because stems will be provided to all students. Teachers should avoid assessing students based on language errors, given that students' sentences may seem disjointed and lack transitions.	Students can be encouraged to use passive voice, for example the stems for questions 2 and 4 can be changed to: "Those data were measured by..." "The implications of these results are..."	Students can be expected to use passive voice and other frequent determinants of high-quality writing (see p. 40)

Example/Non-Example *(Motley, 2016)*

1. The teacher provides an example of a high-quality response to a writing prompt as well as an example of a response that does not meet expectations for the prompt.
2. The teacher leads a whole-group discussion of the characteristics that make the "Example" high quality and the "Non-example" poor quality.
3. Students can then work in partners or groups to identify high-quality and low-quality characteristics of another pair of responses.

Some frequent determinants of high-quality writing that the teacher can touch on or the students can discuss are as follows:

- Proper use of vocabulary   • Inclusion of vocabulary
- Avoidance of colloquial language
- Minimal use of pronouns (such as "it" or "they"), with proper antecedent referencing
- Passive voice   • Avoidance of first-person language

> **WRITING PROMPT: Describe the interactions of body systems involved in gas exchange.**

✔ Example

Air enters through the trachea into the lungs when a person inhales. Oxygen in the air is transported from the lungs into the circulatory system by red blood cells. The red blood cells exchange oxygen for carbon dioxide at the membrane of all the cells of the body. Then the carbon dioxide is transported back to the respiratory system and exhaled.

✗ Non-Example

We breathe in oxygen and breathe out carbon dioxide. It goes in the blood to the brain and other things. We need air to survive and the heart keeps pumping. Circulation. The cells are important too because they transport it. Then the lungs move everything back to where it all started. They do that so the oxygen and carbon dioxide can exchange each other.

WRITING PROMPT:
Compare and contrast conduction and convection.

✔ Example

Conduction and convection are both forms of heat transfer. Conduction involves transfer of heat through direct contact, such as when a metal pot is on a hot stove. In contrast, convection involves heat transfer through a liquid or gas, such as when hot air moves around in an oven. In both processes, heat always moves from a hotter substance to a cooler substance.

✗ Non-Example

Conduction is like when a pot gets hot on the stove, and convection is like hot air. Both get hot. And it's always going from hot to cold.

NEWCOMER/BEGINNER	INTERMEDIATE	ADVANCED	NEARLY FLUENT
Beginning-level writers will be equipped to evaluate minimal features of science writing in English (i.e., some use of capitalization, periods, inclusion of a title or heading, etc.). It would be helpful to convey the purpose of the activity through the use of native-language support, such as native-language text on the same topic as the example.	Students would benefit from additional support (such as native-language text on the same topic as the example) after the exercise to clarify expectations and "where to start." Students can be encouraged to focus on expressing two or three concise ideas in their writing or on maintaining proper verb tenses, for example.	Students should be encouraged to use a variety of sentence structures and include frequent determinants of high-quality writing (see instructions on previous page) to convey complete thoughts in their writing after this exercise.	Students can be expected to convey their thoughts with clarity on a level commensurate with their native English-speaking peers and should be encouraged to focus on maintaining an academic tone where applicable.

Written Conversation

In an activity that really brings science to life, the class works together to brainstorm imaginary attitudes and beliefs as if they were organisms or structures from the current unit of study.

Possible brainstorming sentence frames to begin the activity:

___ probably believes...

___ might say...

One thing ____ would want us to know is...

The students form partnerships, each taking the points of view of related terms. Partner A begins writing a short note to Partner B, who responds by adding a few sentences and sending the letter back. The exchange can last for up to ten minutes, depending on the depth of knowledge and age of the students.

Dear _____,

I see we agree about...

Have you ever considered that...

I disagree about...

You made me think...

Students' notes should be collected for a formative review to ensure the writing accurately addresses the content.

NEWCOMER/BEGINNER	INTERMEDIATE	ADVANCED	NEARLY FLUENT
During the collaboration piece, students should be allowed to observe another student pair. They could complete their writing in their native language, apply English labels to key terms that have been translated into their native language, and then complete one or two sentences with those same key terms.	During the conversation piece, students will likely use a combination of their native language and English if their partner comprehends both languages, but they should be encouraged to write their sentences in English. Stems with past tense verbs are encouraged.	Students' writing should be relatively accurate in terms of verb tense and word choice. Students may not exhibit much abstract thinking due to the "in the moment" nature of the writing task. The focus should remain on content versus grammar and linguistic structures when their writing is evaluated.	Students should be encouraged to respond to their partners by paraphrasing their responses in order to work on listening skills. Students can be expected to complete the writing task on a level commensurate with their non-EL peers, but since this will be a quick write without opportunities for revision, more frequent grammatical errors than normal are to be expected in the writing portion.

ACADEMIC CONVERSATION

Academic conversation is structured dialogue between students about the science content. You have already seen numerous examples of structured student dialogue throughout this book. In this section, we present activities that promote prolonged and detailed discourse about the content of a science lesson.

Academic conversation is important because it provides students an opportunity to analyze and synthesize new ideas without the pressure and finality of producing a written document. This lowers their stress levels and allows their brains to function in optimal conditions. In a quality academic conversation, students forge new connections between concepts and cultivate deep, long-term learning.

Keep in mind, however, that academic conversations must be structured. The process of explaining ideas using new vocabulary can leave students, particularly English learners, unsure of where to start. Because of this, sentence stems are critical to the structure of the conversations. Picture it this way: academic conversation is like learning to ride a bike. The hard part is not actually riding the bike, but getting started. Think of sentence stems as that supportive push — once the wheels are turning and the student is confident, it's all smiles from there. After much practice, speaking academically becomes like…well, riding a bike!

Tap and Talk

1. The teacher gives a printed-out page to students with several different pictures and a word bank. The pictures can be metaphorical representations (such as a library to represent the nucleus of a cell) or pictures of science models (such as mRNA entering a ribosome to represent translation). However, metaphorical representations are particularly effective for this activity because they encourage divergent thinking and rich dialogue.

2. In partners or groups, the students are instructed to take turns pointing to ("tapping") different pictures and identifying the vocabulary word they think each picture represents and why, using the sentence stem:

   I think this picture represents _____ because...   Subjective in a bad way

3. Students continue going in turns until all of the words in the word bank have been used. Once this happens, students are encouraged to identify which pictures might represent multiple words. In the example to the right, there are fewer pictures than words, so some pictures have to represent multiple words.

WORD BANK
active transport
passive transport
facilitated diffusion
ATP
diffusion
osmosis
concentration gradient

eh maybe OK

NOTE: It is important that students are reminded that there are no right answers as long as they justify their reasoning. This promotes participation and allows for more creative, deep thinking.

NEWCOMER/BEGINNER	INTERMEDIATE	ADVANCED	NEARLY FLUENT
Students speak to a native-language peer or an English-speaking peer who is comfortable working with a beginner. Students may choose not to utilize the "because" portion of the stem.	Students share with a native-language partner if possible, and likely use a mix of English and their native language before completing the stem in English.	The stem, visuals, and word bank are sufficient scaffolds for advanced students, but students should be encouraged to use abstract thinking in their analyses and to extend the explanations through the "because" portion of the stem.	Students should be reminded to take their time formulating answers to the more abstract pairings.

WIT Questioning

Students in science classrooms often struggle to give elaborate responses using academic language. By providing students with simple prompts, we can greatly increase their ability to elaborate during both teacher-led discussions and peer interactions in the science classroom. By directly teaching and modeling the use of specific elaboration stems, we give students a tool that can increase their understanding and ability to engage in academic discussions.

1. Create and display a chart with the following stems:

   Why do you think?

   Is there another…?

   Tell me more about…

2. Model for the students how you will use the stems to encourage them to expand their ideas, and how they can use the stems to ask one another questions.

3. Use the prompts consistently during whole-class discussions.

4. Encourage students to use the stems consistently during structured conversations.

NEWCOMER/BEGINNER	INTERMEDIATE	ADVANCED	NEARLY FLUENT
Students quickly become proficient in posing these questions and appreciate the opportunities for participation they provide. It can be helpful for the student to speak to a native-language peer or an English-speaking peer who is comfortable working with a beginner.	Students should be encouraged to use the past tense and elaborate on their ideas where applicable.	Groups should be reminded to allow sufficient wait time (a minimum of ten seconds) after asking a question before expecting a response.	Students should be expected to use complex grammar in their responses.

Expert/Novice *(Seidlitz & Perryman, 2011)*

Students role-play in pairs as an "expert" and a "novice" over a particular topic. The expert is responsible for answering questions about the topic, and the novice is responsible for asking questions and actively listening to the responses.

1. Pairs of students brainstorm possible questions about the topic. This may be facilitated in a whole-group setting to ensure key concepts are covered.

2. The pairs enact a role-play where the "novice" asks the "expert" questions and the expert answers.

> **Novice:** *How do you...?   What is...?   I don't understand why...*
>
> **Expert:** *The first step is...   It is important to...   Let me clarify that...*

3. The novice then paraphrases the expert's advice:
   It sounds like you're saying...

Can you explain why...?

Please clarify your statement about...

4. The teacher randomly chooses partners to enact their role-play in front of the class.

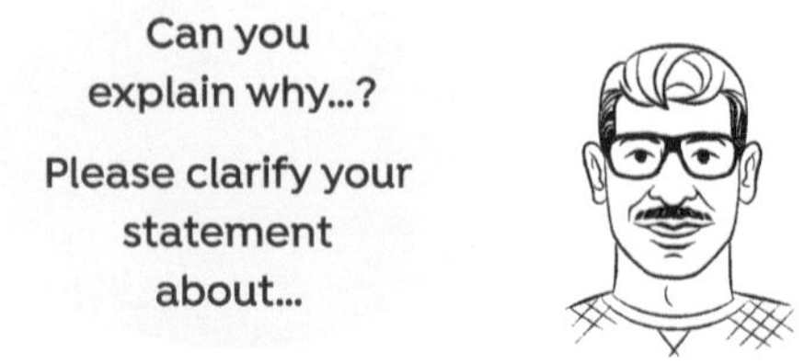

NEWCOMER/BEGINNER	INTERMEDIATE	ADVANCED	NEARLY FLUENT
Students will be more comfortable in the novice role and should be given questions to ask their partner. They may be able to express the gist of their partner's message in a drawing, in a simple English stem, or as a more detailed retelling in their native language.	Students can serve in either role for this strategy but may face challenges with maintaining academic language throughout the exercise. They are able to summarize the gist of their partner's message as the expert. *My partner said...*	Students benefit from being the expert in this exercise because it is an opportunity to practice academic language. As novices, they can help inter-mediate students craft their answers to sound more like an expert.	Students can serve in either role. As a novice, they would benefit from a non-EL or advanced/nearly fluent partner as the expert. When working with an intermediate student, the nearly fluent EL will benefit most as the expert. Partnering a nearly fluent EL with a beginner can be frustrating for both partners.

[Handwritten margin notes: "OK but titles are too power laten" next to item 2; "deficit" with arrow pointing to the Newcomer/Beginner column]

CHAPTER 6
Assessment

Assessments are critical opportunities to gain insight about student learning — not just students' cumulative understanding of concepts, but also the development of inferencing and analytical skills. Students' cumulative understanding is developed through interactions with data as they make connections between experiments and their learning of the natural world, as well as through listening, reading, speaking, and writing opportunities such as those presented in this book. The processing skills of inferencing and analyzing are developed through interactions with data and laboratory investigations, as well as through analysis of previously collected data (such as in Uncover the Picture p. 17, Visual Pre-Read p. 34 and Tales from a Graph p. 39).

Effective science assessments intertwine inferencing and analysis within questions about specific content. For example, an assessment might describe an experiment and present a graph, then ask what the results might mean. To answer the question correctly, the student must be able to decipher and interpret the graph as well as understand the natural phenomena described in the question. The interconnectedness of science concepts and processing skills is essential for the complex reasoning required in advanced science courses and STEM fields.

Standardized assessments in science also frequently embed processing skills within content-based questions. These assessments are often limited in their measurement of student learning, however, because they rely heavily on closed-ended, multiple-choice formats. A notable exception to this are the Advanced Placement (AP) science exams offered through the College Board, which require an extensive (40 to 50 percent) writing component. Writing is not only an essential science skill, but also an opportunity for

students to express their learning in their own terms. This opportunity is particularly important for ELs as they acquire English proficiency. It is in the writing portions that effective science assessments provide opportunities for students to convey content knowledge while demonstrating and practicing processing skills in an open-ended format.

EVIDENCE-BASED REASONING

The ability to form conclusions based on evidence is an essential scientific skill. Accordingly, national associations of science and science education organizations have placed reasoning and evaluation of scientific claims as a top priority in science curriculum (Brown et al., 2010). In the classroom, an evidence-based reasoning approach must be structured to stimulate students' thinking and help them organize their thoughts. While the process of making a claim and supporting it with evidence can and should be collaborative, each student will ultimately create a written product that will reflect their learning. In this way, evidence-based reasoning is essentially an assessment in and of itself, providing invaluable insight into students' conceptualization of the science content.

First, the teacher presents a scientific question to the class. The question should be closed-ended with specific answer choices. The teacher tells the students they will be looking for evidence that will help them answer the question — not trying to immediately answer the question. This is important because it reduces students' stress about finding the "right" answer and lets them focus their thinking on the justification of the answer — the reasoning. At this point and throughout the process, the teacher reminds students that the important thing about this process is not to find the correct answer, but rather to provide thorough justifications that defend the answer.

Evidence-based reasoning is essentially an assessment in and of itself, providing invaluable insight into students' conceptualization of the science content.

Next, students assemble evidence that will help them answer the question. The evidence could be drawn from a laboratory investigation (see following page) or a scientific text, or it could be a synthesis of learning. Evidence could look like a graph or data table, graphic organizer, model or illustration, or even a bulleted list of ideas. It is important that students intentionally gather evidence related to the question. For example, a graphic organizer describing properties of different types of rocks is not likely related to a question about conservation of energy.

Finally, the students answer the question (the claim) with justification (the reasoning). Students are provided with sentence stems to help them reference the evidence while crafting thorough explanations. Students should also be asked to include key vocabulary in their reasoning. The process is described on the next page:

1. First, the teacher presents the question and asks students to discuss what they know about the subject of question using the QSSSA method (see p. 29).

2. Next, the teacher describes different types of evidence the students might want to use to write their claims and reasoning. The students discuss how the evidence is related to the question in partners or groups.

    _____ *is related to the question because...*

3. After assembling the evidence, students verbally justify their claims to their partners or groups using the following structure:

    I think _____ because...

Evidence-Based Reasoning for Laboratory Investigations

The beauty of evidence-based reasoning is that it mirrors the final, formal stages of the scientific process. The "Results and Discussion" section of any peer-reviewed scientific research publication consists of figures presenting objective observations (the evidence) that address a driving question (the question), with conclusions (the claim and reasoning) drawn on the figures.

The QECR model can be used prior to conducting the investigation to drive formation and justification of the hypothesis. Based on a central driving question, students gather their background knowledge related to the subject (the evidence) and formulate a hypothesis (the claim) based on and justified by the evidence (the reasoning).

Students then draft an experimental design and procedures with justification, or the teacher provides the experimental design and procedures and asks students to explain how the design and procedures address the hypothesis. For example, students in groups might each discuss a different component of the experimental design and procedures based on the sentence stem, "This component is important because..."

After following laboratory procedures, students assemble data collecting during the lab in a second evidence section of the lab report. Based on the evidence assembled, students then make a second claim, this time providing a conclusive answer to the driving question. The justification of this claim, including the use of key vocabulary, marks the final part of the laboratory report, and is analogous to the "conclusions" section of a scientific publication.

The QECR model for Laboratory Investigations

PRE-LAB	Question	the question driving the experiment
	Evidence	background content knowledge about the question, clearly indicating key vocabulary
	Claim	the hypothesis answering the question, using key vocabulary
	Reasoning	Justification of the hypothesis, based on the background evidence

Experimental design and procedures (provided by teacher or generated by students), with justification about how the hypothesis is addressed

POST-LAB	Evidence	experimental results, presented graphically or a table
	Claim	the concluded answer to the driving question
	Reasoning	justification of the concluding claim, based on experimental results, including key vocabulary

A description of each component of the laboratory report is provided above.

Search for diagrams of "the scientific method" in any web image search, and you will invariably come across flow charts detailing all of the components above, which all end in "publishing" or "reporting." In the context of your class, this is the writing of the laboratory report. However, what is often under-discussed in school and university is what happens after publication: reception by the scientific community. This is a stage known as consensus-building, where scientists provide their own interpretations of the data or determine whether the presented conclusions agree with the results of previous or future experiments. This is the part of the scientific process in which theories become accepted as facts. The theories that the Earth revolves around the Sun and that species evolve based on changing reproductive success in changing environments are also considered facts because there is a broad scientific consensus, meaning that other experiments and interpretations of experiments agree with the theories.

Consensus-building is just as important in the classroom as it is in the symposium. Thus, it is important for students to share their conclusions and their justifications with their classmates and to form a class-wide understanding of the phenomena driving the experiment. To facilitate rich discussion and reduce students' stress that may be associated with sharing their work with others, try the following:

1. Students share their concluding claim in small groups (two to four students each) using the sentence stem, *"I believe... because..."* Students should be encouraged to point to their evidence figures while sharing their reasoning with their groups.

2. Groups are asked to prepare a report of a consensus reasoning or, if there were significant differences between findings and reasoning, to report multiple ideas.

3. A group reporter is designated, and each group reporter shares the findings with the rest of the class using the sentence stems, *"We found that... because..."* or, *"We were divided between _____ and _____ because..."*

4. The teacher paraphrases and points out connections between groups' responses, then asks each student to write a two- to three-sentence consensus beginning with the sentence stem, *"Based on the class's findings, I conclude..."* Importantly, the teacher should ask students to include key vocabulary in their consensus.

WHAT TO DO INSTEAD OF A SECTION REVIEW

All too often, teachers and students experience frustration when successful daily demonstrations of learning do not translate into commensurate success on the unit or benchmark exam. Section reviews are therefore important for students to process large amounts of content learned over the course of several days or weeks and to understand how their daily learning fits into a bigger picture. Effective section reviews do not stop at stimulating recall of isolated, simple facts, but instead have students think about the connections between facts. Such section reviews stimulate deep thinking for all learners, but ELs and struggling learners who might have missed key pieces of information during the unit benefit especially from the opportunity to understand the context of learning. Instead of doing a multiple choice or matching review, consider doing one of the next three activities, which encourage students to generate connections within and between units.

Vocab Connection Web

Working in pairs, students are provided a list of vocabulary words from the unit. Students are instructed to choose two words at a time and discuss how they are related to one another using the sentence stem, *"_____ and _____ are related because..."* Students then write each word in a circle and record how they are related underneath a line connecting the circle. The next word is then written in another circle, and a line is drawn from either of the first two words with the same discussion and recording of the two words' relationships as before. New words continue to be added to the web until all of the assigned words have been completed.

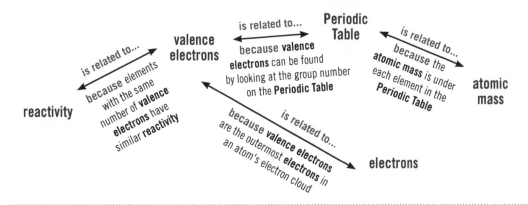

What I Know/What I Wonder

1. The teacher divides the unit into specific topics and displays the title of each topic at the top of chart paper or posters hung around the room.

2. Students are given sticky notes of two different colors and asked to write something they know about each topic on a sticky note of one color (with the sentence stem, "What I know about _____ is...") and something they are unsure about or wonder about each topic on a sticky note of the other color (with the sentence stem, "What I wonder about _____ is...").

3. Students first place their "What I wonder" sticky notes on each poster.

4. Next, students are instructed to read the "What I wonder" sticky notes.

5. They are then told to place their "What I know" sticky notes on the chart paper. If their "What I know" sticky note addresses one of the "What I wonder" sticky notes from another student, they should put it on top of that sticky note.

6. The teacher collects any unaddressed "What I wonder" sticky notes and leads a class discussion to answer the question(s).

7. Students are then instructed to choose two topics to browse and write a short description about their learning, beginning with the sentence stem, "What I now understand about _____ is..."

Student Teaching Stations

1. The teacher assigns each student a vocabulary word or concept from the unit and gives the students a few minutes to create visuals describing their words or concepts.

2. Students are then placed into groups of three and each assigned a letter: A, B, or C.

3. The "A" students describe to their groups how their visuals relate to the words or concepts using the sentence stem, "This visual relates to _____ because..."

4. Each "A" student rotates to a new group so that each group consists of the original "B" and "C" students and a new "A" student.

5. "B" students then explain their visuals using the sentence stem above and rotate to a new group, so that each group consists of the original "C" student and a new "B" and "A" student.

6. The "C" student then presents his/her word to the group and the original groups come back together.

7. Once back together, the group creates a list of all the words or concepts they saw (each group will have seen six in total).

8. Working together, the group then writes a paragraph or two incorporating all six words.

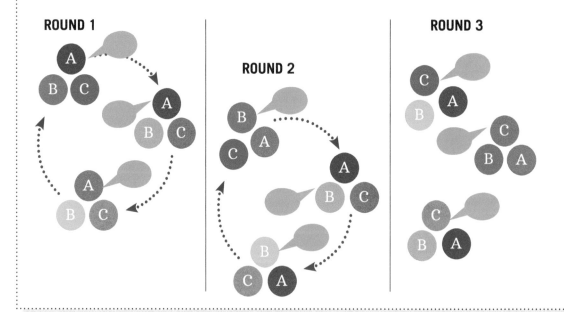

ACCOMMODATED TESTS

Accommodations that specifically support ELs on state, district, and campus-wide assessments vary based on policies that change over time. Whether certain accommodations are allowed on certain assessments should be discussed with campus and district testing coordinators before providing the accommodations. The accommodations that may be allowed on some assessments (such as the use of a dictionary) should be promoted in the classroom on a regular basis to maximize each student's chances of fully utilizing the resource when they take a standardized assessment.

As previously described, it is paramount that students are given the opportunity to express their learning in an open-ended format whenever available. Classroom assessments can therefore provide free-response questions, which can readily be accommodated with sentence stems and word banks. When designing classroom assessments, it is also important to include many visuals. This serves to both accommodate the text and develop students' higher-order thinking and inferencing skills. Effective science assessments require students to think deeply while supporting their linguistic needs.

WHAT ASSESSMENTS WON'T TELL YOU

Formal assessments — especially those that rely heavily on multiple-choice or closed-ended questions — will never give the full picture of a student's potential or language proficiency. Whatever data each assessment produces, it is imperative that we do not let any past or current assessment results shape our perspective of what our students can produce in the future.

We must foster a growth mindset in our classes and use assessment results to pinpoint the small steps that can be taken toward incremental improvement.

In my class, students tracked their assessment data in their notebooks (as good scientists would!). With each assessment, I would ask students to focus not on whether or not they passed or received an advanced score, but whether or not they performed a little bit better than the previous tests. Then I would instruct them to analyze their results to determine which actions they could take to improve their performance by a little bit next time.

This played an important role in shaping self-image, motivation, and, eventually, end-of-year performance. I had students who had not passed a single state assessment, but did at the end of the year. I also had students who went outside their comfort zones and began to push themselves in ways they had never done before.

One such student, Melissa, had never taken an honors class, and she was testing in my ninth-grade biology class just below the passing threshold for the state assessment. Melissa was flagged to be pulled into an intervention class with the intent of bringing her from just below passing to just above passing. I decided to take a different approach. I communicated with Melissa, telling her that continued growth is what really matters. She took to this message. Yes, she improved past the passing threshold, and yes, she passed her state assessment at the end of the year. But she didn't stop there. The next year, for the first time, Melissa enrolled in honors classes, including my AP Biology class. She struggled of course, but she maintained a mindset of continuous improvement and began thriving. Now in her senior year, Melissa is still thriving in the most advanced classes and is aggressively applying to the top colleges. When the communication changed from "meeting standards" to "slow, steady growth," Melissa began to visualize success and believe in herself.

terrible
story

If we as teachers invest in our students, especially our English learners, we will see that they are all capable of contributing to global funds of knowledge and transforming the scientific discipline in their own time and in their own ways.

Language Proficiency Differentiation Guide

Warm-Ups

Uncover the Picture

Language Anticipation Guide

Visual-Description Matchup

Building Background

Vocab Breakdown

Gearing Up for the Guiding Question

Caption the Comic

Interactive Lecture

QSSSA

Complete the Picture

Questioning Conversation

Academic Reading

Visual Pre-Read

Three Reads, Three Questions

"Gimme Five" Summarization Strategy

Academic Writing

Tales from a Graph

Example/Non-Example

Written Conversation

Academic Conversation

Tap and Talk

WIT Quiestioning

Expert/Novice

Warm-Ups

ACTIVITY	NEWCOMER/BEGINNER	INTERMEDIATE	ADVANCED	NEARLY FLUENT
Uncover the Picture The teacher projects an image to the class that is partially covered. The image is slowly uncovered while students list things they see. The teacher pauses three times to let students make predictions about the image.	Students are each provided a copy of the image and are asked to identify components of the image by correctly labeling them with assistance from a word bank. Students may choose to translate terms into their native language. *I see a...*	Teachers give students an appropriate amount of wait time before asking them to identify components of the image and add descriptors. *I noticed a...*	Students could be expected to elaborate on their predictions using more complex grammar structures. *It is significant that ____ because...*	Students should be encouraged to discuss more abstract ideas related to the image. *I'm wondering _____ because...*
Language Anticipation Guide Students are presented with academic terms and phrases that will be discussed in the day's lesson alongside possible definitions of the terms. Students select whether the stated definition is the true definition in the context of the day's lesson. This is particularly effective to familiarize students with "mortar" words that are not taught explicitly and can have different definitions in non-academic versus academic contexts.	Students complete one to two items using a native-language resource for support. *I choose (true/false) for number 1.*	Students complete both Before and After columns with teacher support as needed for non-key terms within the statements. They discuss any adjustments made to "before" predictions using the following stem: *I chose (true/false) for the word ___. Now I think...*	Students complete both Before and After columns with minimal assistance. They discuss any adjustments made to "before" predictions using this stem: *At first I thought number ___ was (true / false) but now I think ____ because...*	Students complete both Before and After columns without assistance. They discuss any adjustments made to "before" predictions after reading using the following stem: *After reading, I changed my answer on number ___ to (true/false) based on...*
Visual-Description Matchup Designed to help students connect visuals to new vocabulary terms, this strategy increases comprehension while fostering relationships among students through interaction and movement.	Students may locate their partners more easily if they are provided the visual portion of the pairing. *My card shows (a/the)....* *Your card shows (a/the)....*	After clarification of pronunciation of key terms, students complete this activity without further accommodation, though errors in verbal communication are to be expected. *My card shows (a/the) ____. It matches the word...*	Advanced students need the opportunity to practice new content-area vocabulary, so their stems should be designed to promote academic language use. *I think our cards match because...* *They might be associated with the term...*	Nearly fluent students benefit from multiple opportunities to practice new vocabulary with a native-speaking partner when possible. Their stems should be designed to elicit more complex grammar and additional detail. *I think our cards match because...*

Building Background

ACTIVITY	NEWCOMER/BEGINNER	INTERMEDIATE	ADVANCED	NEARLY FLUENT
Vocab Breakdown The teacher breaks the vocabulary words into prefixes, roots, and suffixes and assigns the parts of a vocabulary word to each member of a group. The teacher also provides the students with the meaning of each prefix, suffix, and root. Students are given two to three minutes to draw a picture to represent each word part.	The visual nature of this task minimizes the accommodations necessary for students. They should be allowed to remain silent during the group discussion and should be allowed to utilize a native-language resource to complete the activity.	Students utilize simple sentence stems to participate in the group discussion and complete the individual/pair discussion with assistance from native-language or peer resource as needed. *I drew a _____ because...*	Students should be encouraged to seek clarification of any classmate's answer when needed by using the WIT questioning method (See p. 45) *Why do you think?* *Is there another...?* *Tell me more about...*	Students should be encouraged to construct multiple responses for the same prefix, suffix, etc. where possible. *I discovered _____.*
Gearing up for the Guiding Question Students are presented the central question of the lesson (the guiding question) and the key vocabulary of the day, and are instructed to discuss the question with a partner, using the key vocabulary, for three minutes before attempting to answer it. Each vocabulary word should be accompanied by an explanatory, text-minimal visual and pronunciation should be modeled.	During the writing component, students can apply labels to any "big picture" visual that pertains to the lesson and then complete simple sentence stems that reflect the guiding question using a word bank for key vocabulary.	Frequent errors should be expected in conversation and in writing, due to the speed of the activity. Students may need to use a combination of their native language and English during the paired conversation if their partner comprehends both languages, but should be encouraged to complete the writing in English (using resources such as the word bank).	Students are able to explain the reasoning for the category generated using correct sentence structure and grammar. *We elected to create the category of _____ because...*	Students are able to explain the reasoning for the categories generated using correct sentence structure and grammar. *We elected to create the category of _____ because...*
Caption the Comic Present students with a series of three to five images in the format of a comic strip (logically sequenced with a cause-and-effect relationship). Instruct the students to write captions in narrative language that describe each image and connects the images together in a story. Sentence stems can help to focus students.	Before the lesson, students can be provided native language resources related to the topic. Students should be permitted to complete their work in their native language.	Before the lesson, students can be provided native language resources related to the topic. Students should be able to complete this task with minimal support because stems will be provided to all students. *I drew a _____ because...*	Students benefit from teacher modeling of the use of transitional and sequential language. Students can be expected to perform like non-EL students in this task.	Students can be expected to perform like non-EL students in this task.

WIDA/ELPA21 Beginner 1 & 2, Intermediate 3, Advanced 4, Nearly Fluent 5

Interactive Lecture

ACTIVITY	NEWCOMER/BEGINNER	INTERMEDIATE	ADVANCED	NEARLY FLUENT
QSSSA The teacher presents the question to the class, pausing at the end to give the students time to think. The teacher provides students with a specific response signal to indicate when they are ready to answer and a sentence stem to use for their response. After sharing their responses with partners, students are chosen randomly to share with the whole group.	Students speak to a native-language peer, or an English-speaking peer who is comfortable working with a beginner.	Students should be able to complete the stem before working with partners. The share portion should help them clarify their thinking. They might need to be reminded that the stem is available when sharing with the whole group.	Students are encouraged to use the most complex stem provided or create their own sentence(s).	Students should be expected to use the most complex stem provided or create their own sentence(s).
Complete the Picture A half-covered image related to the content is given to students. Students are instructed to complete the second half of the visual to their best estimation. Students then have a structured conversation about how they completed the drawing and why they completed it the way they did.	The visual nature of this task minimizes the accommodations necessary for students, beyond those typically necessary for a structured conversation (see QSSSA). *I drew (a/the) _____.*	Students should be able to complete this task with minimal support because stems will be provided to all students. *I drew _____ because...*	Students can be expected to perform like non-EL students in this task. *In my drawing, I included ____ because...*	Students can be expected to perform like non-EL students in this task.
Questioning Conversation This activity provides a structure for students to craft their own questions about the content. Students individually develop a question using a sentence stem then develop hypotheses to answer their own questions.	Students should be able to complete the sentence stem after working with their partners. They should not be expected to speak in front of the whole group unless they volunteer.	Students should be able to complete the stem before working with their partners. The share portion should help them clarify their thinking. They might need to be reminded that the stem is available when sharing with the whole group..	Provided they are very familiar and have sufficient background knowledge with the materials, students should be able to engage in these conversations with minimal support. They should be encouraged to seek clarification from the teacher or their partners when needed.	Teacher modeling of the expectations for conversation should be sufficient support for students, who should be reminded to seek clarification as needed.

Academic Reading

ACTIVITY	NEWCOMER/BEGINNER	INTERMEDIATE	ADVANCED	NEARLY FLUENT
Visual Pre-Read The teacher presents a text with an accompanying visual. Before reading, students are instructed to analyze the title of the text as well as the visual and make predictions about the content of the text. Students discuss in partners or groups.	Teacher models the use of the stems and pronounces the words found in titles, captions, and subtitles. Allow students to use native language/ drawing to express comprehension of the visual material.	Teacher models the use of the stems before students discuss the stems with their partners. Speaking with partners should help them clarify their thinking and provide an opportunity for language practice.	Allow students time to rehearse their responses before sharing with the group. They might choose to use their own words instead of the stems.	Students should be encouraged to use a variety of sentence structures and should, after practice, be able to pronounce academic terms correctly.
Three Reads, Three Questions Students read short (1-3 paragraph) text three times, responding to a different sentence stem each time.	Provide newcomer students with a translation of the article in their native language (for example, using the Google Chrome translation feature). Additionally, provide the students a simple outline of the article in English that contains the key terms. The newcomer student might observe a pair composed of either ELs and/or native English speakers, then complete the writing in his/her native language, with key terms translated into English.	Students should be provided with a graphic organizer or a simple outline of the article in English that contains the key terms. It is helpful for the teacher to pre-teach the vocabulary and pronounce any key terms that the students may struggle with while reading the text.	Students can be provided with a graphic organizer to support comprehension of the text.	Students should be provided with visual supports and modeling of pronunciation if the text is on a topic with which they have very little familiarity.
"Gimme Five" Summarization Strategy A "Gimme Five" summary consists of five facts from a reading, counted off on each finger until the entire fist has been shared.	Students should be provided with an adapted or native-language version of the text before reading the grade-level text in English. Students should highlight two or three facts from either text.	Students can be provided with an adapted text and given time to write down their summaries before sharing.	Students should be provided time to request clarification for unfamiliar terms found within text.	Students should be encouraged to try to select more significant rather than less significant facts in their "Gimme Five" summaries.

WIDA/ELPA21 Beginner 1 & 2, Intermediate 3, Advanced 4, Nearly Fluent 5

Academic Writing

ACTIVITY	NEWCOMER/BEGINNER	INTERMEDIATE	ADVANCED	NEARLY FLUENT
Tales from a Graph The teacher provides students with a high quality example of the assigned writing, along with an example that does not meet the expectations for that exercise. The class works together to identify what makes the example one to imitate, and why the non-example is not what is desired.	Students could be expected to label a graph using labels provided in a word bank and should be able to use the terms in pre-constructed sentence frames. Simplified stems could include the following: *The title of the graph is...* *The X-axis measures...* *The Y-axis measures...* *One thing that changed is...* *The scientist can conclude that....*	Students would benefit from additional support, such as native-language text on the same topic as the example after the exercise to clarify expectations and "where to start." They could be encouraged to focus on expressing two or three concise ideas in their writing or on maintaining proper verb tenses, for example.	Students should be encouraged to use a variety of sentence structures and to convey complete thoughts in their writing after this exercise.	Students can be expected to convey their thoughts with clarity on a level commensurate with their native English-speaking peers and should be encouraged to focus on supporting their thoughts with evidence where applicable.
Example/ Non-Example Students write from a first-person perspective about the academic concept and are faced with making decisions that have a fortunate or unfortunate impact.	Beginning-level writers will be equipped to evaluate minimal features of science writing in English (i.e., some use of capitalization, periods, inclusion of a title or heading, etc.). It would be helpful to convey the purpose of the activity through the use of native-language support, such as native-language text on the same topic as the example.	Students' writing should maintain the "voice" chosen at the beginning of the exercise. Because the focus is on content and not structure, it is expected that students will have frequent errors, particularly in terms of verb tense and vague pronouns.	Students' writing should be relatively accurate in terms of verb tense and word choice. Students may not exhibit much abstract thinking due to the "in the moment" nature of the writing task.	Students should compose pieces that are grade-level appropriate with minimal errors that result from unfamiliar contexts. While their pieces may be shorter than those of non-ELL classmates, the quality of the work should be similar. However, since this is a "quick write" without opportunity for revision, more frequent errors than normal are to be expected.
Written Conversation Students write from various points of view, audiences to whom they are writing, formats for the writing, and topics within the content.	During the collaboration piece, students should be allowed to observe another student pair. They could complete their writing in their native language, apply English labels to key terms that have been translated into their native language, and then complete one or two sentences with those same key terms.	During the conversation piece, students will likely use a combination of their native language and English if their partner comprehends both languages, but they should be encouraged to write their sentences in English. Stems with past tense verbs are encouraged.	Students' writing should be relatively accurate in terms of verb tense and word choice. Students may not exhibit much abstract thinking due to the "in the moment" nature of the writing task. Evaluation should focus on content versus grammar and linguistic structures.	Students should be encouraged to respond to their partners by paraphrasing their responses in order to work on listening skills. Students can be expected to complete the writing task on a level commensurate with non-EL peers, but since this will be a quick write without revision, more frequent grammatical errors than normal are to be expected.

WIDA/ELPA21 Beginner 1 & 2, Intermediate 3, Advanced 4, Nearly Fluent 5

62 TEACHING SCIENCE to ELs

Academic Conversation

ACTIVITY	NEWCOMER/BEGINNER	INTERMEDIATE	ADVANCED	NEARLY FLUENT
Tap and Talk The teacher gives a printed-out page to students with several different pictures and a word bank. In partners or groups, the students are instructed to take turns pointing to ("tapping") different pictures and identifying the vocabulary word they think each picture represents and why.	Students speak to a native-language peer or an English-speaking peer who is comfortable working with a beginner. Students may choose not to utilize the "because" portion of the stem.	Students share with a native-language partner if possible, and likely use a mix of English and their native language before completing the stem in English.	The stem, visuals, and word bank are sufficient scaffolds for advanced students, but students should be encouraged to use abstract thinking in their analyses and to extend the explanations through the "because" portion of the stem.	Students should be reminded to take their time formulating answers to the more abstract pairings.
WIT Questioning Create and display a chart with sentence stems. Model for the students how you will use the stems, and how they can use the stems to ask one another questions. Use the prompts consistently during whole-class discussions.Encourage students to use the stems consistently during structured conversations.	Students quickly become proficient in posing these questions and appreciate the opportunities for participation they provide. It can be helpful for the student to speak to a native-language peer or an English-speaking peer who is comfortable working with a beginner.	Students should be encouraged to use the past tense and elaborate on their ideas where applicable.	Groups should be reminded to allow sufficient wait time (a minimum of ten seconds) after asking a question before expecting a response.	Students should be expected to use complex grammar in their responses.
Expert/Novice Students are divided into pairs. One student takes on the role of an expert and the other a novice in a particular situation. The expert responds to questions asked by the novice, modeling academic language.	Students will be more comfortable in the novice role and should be given questions to ask their partners. They may be able to express the gist of their partners' messages in drawings, in simple English stems, or as more detailed retellings in their native language.	Students can play either role for this strategy but may face challenges maintaining academic language throughout the exercise. Novices are able to summarize the gist of their expert partners' messages. *My partner said...*	Students benefit from being the expert in this exercise because it is an opportunity to practice academic language. As novices, they can help intermediate students craft their answers to sound more like experts.	Students can play either role. As novices, they would benefit from non-EL or nearly fluent partners as the experts. When working with intermediate students, the nearly fluent will benefit most by playing the expert. Partnering nearly fluent ELs with beginners can be frustrating for both partners.

WIDA/ELPA21 Beginner 1 & 2, Intermediate 3, Advanced 4, Nearly Fluent 5

Appendix L ~~~

See Yourself as a Scientist

Exposure to STEM role models that students can identify with goes a long way toward helping the students see themselves as scientists. Each time they hear about people such as Easton Chapelle, a teenager who engineered a prosthetic arm using LEGO and a 3D printer then provided the plans online for free, or about an underfunded robotics team that triumphed unexpectedly, it serves as a reminder that they, too, could pioneer the next big discovery or defy the odds.

Specifically highlighting the contributions of non-traditional and immigrant scientists magnifies that message for English learners, who can identify with the additional effort required of those whose work was conducted in their second or third language. A quick internet search will yield extensive examples of scientists, inventors, and other intellectual pioneers who have overcome challenges akin to those faced by many of our ELs, and the number of those stories will continue to grow. When students learn that, between the year 2000 and now, 35 percent of Nobel Prizes won by the United States have been earned by immigrants, it serves as a reminder that diversity of thought and experience should be celebrated and that their achievements need not be limited by language proficiency. Students' STEM role models should not be limited to Edison and Newton and Salk. Encouraging them to seek out inspiring stories like those shown here builds resilience, as each person serves as a testament to the power of perseverance, effort, and drive — skills all students can cultivate and utilize to achieve their goals. And who knows? If someday they are profiled as the next great chemist or astrophysicist, they just might say it was in your class that they first believed it possible.

Who knows? If someday your students are profiled as the next great chemist or astrophysicist, they just might say it was in your class that they first believed it possible.

Mary Anning was only eleven years old in 1811 when she became a fossil hunter in England. Having minimal formal education, she began to study subjects such as geology, anatomy, and paleontology on her own. Eventually scientists traveled from all over to work alongside Mary, and her contributions shaped our understanding of marine life during the Jurassic period.

Among his many accomplishments, **Albert Einstein** gave the world its "most famous equation." He was born in Germany and studied in Switzerland before visiting the United States in 1933. As Hitler came to power, Einstein was forced to seek refugee status due to his Jewish heritage. He became a U.S. citizen in 1940.

Marie Skłodowska was born in Poland but completed her studies in Paris, where she met her husband and colleague Pierre Curie. They shared the 1903 Nobel Prize in Physics, and Marie garnered another after Pierre's death, making her the first person to ever win the award twice. Their daughter, Irene Curie, also shared a Nobel with her husband, Frederic Joliot.

Shinya Yamanaka was born in Japan, completed some of his research in the U.S., and recently won a Nobel Prize for his pioneering efforts in stem cell research. He began his career as a surgeon but then switched to science after his father passed away unexpectedly. He believes making mistakes is one of the best parts of research because it gives him the chance to learn something new. Dr. Yamanaka hopes his efforts will one day save many more lives than he ever could have through surgery.

Mark Richards was born in the U.K. to Jamaican parents. He always had a knack for chemistry and for music, so he became both a scientist and a DJ. He's currently researching and developing instruments to monitor air pollution for a tech company he co-founded, while also producing music as DJ Kemist under his own label.

Sabrina Pasterski is a Cuban-American physicist whose work has been cited by Stephen Hawking. She graduated from MIT at the top of her class — and in only three years — before continuing her studies at Harvard. She builds and flies planes in her spare time.

These are good(ish)

Appendix II

Turning Closed-Ended Questions into Open-Ended Questions

Definite-Answer ("Closed-Ended") Question	Open-Ended Question
Is it A or B? ***Example:*** *If temperature increases, does pressure increase or decrease?*	**Why** would it be A? *Why would pressure increase when temperature increases?* **How** does A happen? *How does increasing temperature cause pressure to increase?* **Predict** what would happen if it was B instead of A. *What would it look like if temperature increased and pressure decreased?*
What is (the fact)? ***Example:*** *What is a mutation?*	**How** does (the fact) happen? *How does a change in DNA happen?* **How** would (this fact) relate to (that fact)? *What would a change in DNA have to do with protein structure?* **Why** is (the fact) important? *Why is it important that DNA can change?* **Predict** how (other fact) would be affected if (this fact) did not happen. *How would evolution be affected if mutations did not happen?*
List (the steps). ***Example:*** *List the steps to finding grams of product from grams of reactant.*	**How** do (the steps) relate to each other? *What does finding moles have to do with finding grams?* **Why** does (the first step) come before (the second step)? *Why do you have to find moles of the product before you can find grams of the product?* **Predict** what would happen if (any given step) was absent/altered. *What would happen to the number of moles of product if the molar mass of reactant was incorrectly calculated?*

Definite-Answer ("Closed-Ended") Question	Open-Ended Question
List (the factors). *Example:* *List the causes for hypertension.*	**How** could you distinguish (these factors) from (those factors)? *How are causes for hypertension different from causes for diabetes?* **How** do (these factors) contribute to (that fact)? *How do the causes for hypertension result in increased blood pressure?* **Predict** what would happen if (these factors) had (this property). *Predict what would happen if stress and old age also reduced insulin secretion.* **Justify** why (this factor) is more impactful than (that factor). *Justify why chronic stress is more likely to cause hypertension than old age.*
Identify (the factor). *Example:* *Identify which object is at rest.*	**How** would you identify (the factor) from this selection? *How would you find the object that is at rest?* **Describe** the properties which lead you to identify (this factor). *Describe how you know object C is at rest.* **How** would you identify (this factor) if it was altered in this way? *How would you identify which object is at rest if you were not given the magnitude of forces acting upon it?*

Appendix III

Prefixes, Suffixes, and Roots (Morphemes) Commonly Used in Science

Morpheme	Simple Definition	Morpheme	Simple Definition	Morpheme	Simple Definition
a- or an-	not	glyco-	carbohydrate (sugar)	-plasm	water or liquid
aero-	air (O_2)	hetero-	different	-polar	to one side
amin-	nitrogen	homo-	same	poly-	many
aqua	water or liquid	hydro-	water	post-	after
-ase	enzyme	hyper-	over	pre- or pro-	before
auto-	self	hypo-	under	retro-	reverse
bi-	two	inter-	between	semi-	half
bio-	life	intra-	within	solu-	dissolved
chrom-	color	iso-	equal	-some or -soma	body
cis-	same side	-kinesis	movement	sub-	under or within
co-	together or with	lipo-	lipids or fat	sym-	together
cyt-	cell	lys- or lyt-	break apart	synthesis	build up
di-	two	macro-	big	telo-	distance
emit-	release	micro-	small	terra-	land
endo-	into or inside	mono-	one	therm-	heat
equ-	equal	multi-	many	-tion or -sion	process of
eu-	good or true	nuc-	in the nucleus	trans-	opposite sides
exo-	out of or outside	-ose	carbohydrate (sugar)	tri-	three
extra-	outside	oxi-	oxygen	trop-	grow
fission	break open	oxid-	electron loss	troph-	energy
fusion	come together	-philic	likes	uni-	one
gen-	DNA	-phobic	does not like	zoo-	animal
geo-	rocks or dirt	photo-	light		

Appendix IV

Spanish-English Science Cognates

Words Related to the Scientific Method and Experimentation

Spanish	English
balanzas	balance
calculadora(s)	calculator(s)
centímetro(s)	centimeter(s)
cilindro(s) graduado(s)	graduated cylinder(s)
computadora(s)	computer(s)
equipo	equipment
experimento(s)	experiments
hipótesis	hypothesis
instrucción(es)	instruction(s)
instrumento(s)	instrument(s)
laboratorio	laboratory
material(es)	material(s)
método(s)	method(s)
metro(s)	meter(s)
microscopio(s)	microscope(s)
observación(es)	observation(s)
origen	origin
referencia(s)	reference(s)
teoría(s)	theory(ies)
termómetro(s)	thermometer(s)
título	title
tubo(s)	tube(s)

Words Used for Data Analysis

Spanish	English
axis	axis
centro	center
ciclo	cycle
círculo(s)	circle(s)
color	color
concepto	concept
constante	constant
datos	data
diagrama	diagram
figura	figure
fórmula(s)	formula(s)
función(es)	function(s)
gráfica(s)	graphic(s)
tabla(s)	table(s)

Questioning Verbs

Spanish	English
analizar	analyze
clasificar	classify
comunicar	communicate
describir	describe
estimar	estimate
evaluar	evaluate
explicar	explain
extrapolar	extrapolate
identificar	identify
listar	list
observar	observe
obtener	obtain
organizar	organize
planear	plan
producir	produce
transformar	transform
usar	use

Science Subjects

Spanish	English
biología	biology
botánica	botany
ciencia	science
física	physics
geología	geology
meteriología	meteorology
química	chemistry

"Mortar" Words Commonly Used in Science Texts

Spanish	English	Spanish	English
artificial	artificial	inferenza(cias)	inference(s)
característica(s)	characteristic(s)	información	information
componente(s)	component(s)	interacción(es)	interaction(s)
conclusión(es)	conclusion(s)	límite	limit
consistencia	consistency	natural	natural
descripción(es)	description(s)	normal	normal
diferente	different	objeto(s)	object(s)
específico	specific	parte(s)	part(s)
estructura(s)	structure(s)	porcentaje	percent
evento(s)	event(s)	presencia	presence
evidencia	evidence	propiedad(es)	property(ies)
externo(s)	external	proteger	protect
fenómeno(s)	phenomenon(a)	simple	simple
general	general	sistema(s)	system(s)
grupo(s)	group(s)	término(s)	term(s)
idea(s)	idea(s)	tipo(s)	type(s)
impacto	impact	total	total
importante	important	variedad	variety
incluyendo	including		

Science Vocabulary Words

Spanish	English
agricultura	agriculture
aire	air
animal(es)	animal(s)
área	area
atmósfera	atmosphere
átomo(s)	atom(s)
biomass	biomass
calcio	calcium
caloría(s)	calorie(s)
carbono	carbon
célula(s)	cell(s)
cinética	kinetic
conservación	conservation
consumidor(es)	consumer(s)
dieta	diet
distancia	distance
ecosistema	ecosystem
electricidad	electricity
elemento(s)	element(s)
endotérmico	endothermic
energía	energy
espacio	space
especies	species

Spanish	English
estímulo(s)	stimulus(i)
exotérmico	exothermic
extinción	extinction
fase(s)	phase(s)
frecuencia	frequency
fuerza	force
galaxia	galaxy
gene(s)	gene(s)
generación(es)	generations
genético/a	genetic
hidrógeno	hydrogen
humano	human
interdependencia	interdependence
mamífero(s)	mammal(s)
materia	matter
mecaníca	mechanical
medicina	medicine
mineral(es)	mineral(s)
movimiento	movement
naturaleza	nature
nitrógeno	nitrogen
nutrición	nutrition
océano(s)	ocean(s)

Spanish	English
órbita(s)	orbit(s)
organismo(s)	organism(s)
órgano(s)	organ(s)
oxígeno	oxygen
planta(s)	plant(s)
plástico(s)	plastic(s)
posición(es)	position(s)
potencial	potential
proteína	protein
radioactivo	radioactive
recesivo/a	recessive
reproducción	reproduction
rotación	rotation
sistema solar	solar system
sistema(s) de órganos	organ system(s)
sólido(s)	solid(s)
solución(es)	solution(s)
sucesión ecología	ecological succession
Tabla Periódica	Periodic Table
universo	universe
vitamin(es)	vitamin(s)
volcán	volcano

Appendix V

Lesson Plan Template

Learning Standard/ Student Expectation		
Content Objective *Student-friendly, aligned to learning standard*		
Writing Objective *Essential question to demonstrate mastery of content objective, incorporating vocabulary*	**Question/Stem**	**Essential Vocabulary** • • •
Text(s) to Read *Reading passages, graphs/ diagrams for analysis, review of notes, lab protocols, etc.*	**Text(s)**	**Thinking Prompts**
Discussions *Prompts for small-group structured conversations*	**Questions/Stems**	**Accompanying Visual(s)**
Warm-Up/Background Builder Activity		
Reflection *Today the students...* *I realized...*		

Sources

Beene, T. (2017). *Teaching Social Studies to ELLs.* Irving, TX: Seidlitz Education.

Billingsley, J. (2015). *Making Words REAL: Proven Strategies for Building Academic Vocabulary Fast.* Abingdon, UK: Routledge.

Bloom, B. M., Englehart, E., Furst, E. H., Hill, W., and Krathwohl, D. (1956). *Taxonomy of educational objectives: The classification of educational goals.* New York: McKay.

Brown, N. J. S., Furtak, E. M., Timms, M., Nagashima, S. O., & Wilson, M. (2010). The evidence-based reasoning framework: Assessing scientific reasoning. *Educational Assessment, 15(3-4),* 123-141.

Fleenor, S. (2018, June 26). Guest post: Teaching the language of science. Retrieved from http://larryferlazzo.edublogs.org/2018/06/26/guest-post-teaching-the-language-of-science/.

Head, M., & Readence, J. (1986). Anticipation guides: Meaning through prediction. In E. Dishner, T. Bean, J. Readence, & D. Moore (Eds.), *Reading in the Content Areas (2nd ed.)* (pp. 229-234). Dubuque, IA: Kendall Hunt.

Johnson, B. E., & Zabrucky, K. M. (2011). Improving middle and high school students' comprehension of science texts. International *Journal of Elementary Education, 4(1),* 19-31.

Manring, M. M., & Calhoun, J. H. (2011). Biographical sketch: Fuller Albright, MD 1900-1969. *Clinical Orthopaedics and Related Research,* 469, 2092-2095.

Motley, N. (2016). *Talk, Read, Talk, Write (2nd Ed).* Irving, TX: Seidlitz Education.

Kaldenberg, E. R., Watt, S. J., & Therrien, W. J. (2015). Reading instruction in science for students with learning disabilities: A meta-analysis. *Learning Disability Quarterly, 38(3),* 160-173.

Patterson, A., Roman, D., Friend, M., Osborne, J., & Donovan, B. (2018). Reading for meaning: The foundational knowledge every teacher of science should have. *International Journal of Science Education, 40(3),* 291-307.

Seidlitz, J., & Perryman, B. (2011). *7 steps to a language-rich interactive classroom: Research-based strategies for engaging all students.* Irving, TX: Seidlitz Education.

Photo credits:

STEPHEN FLEENOR is an Educational Consultant with Seidlitz Education. He earned his Ph.D. in Developmental Neurobiology from the University of Oxford before serving science students as a teacher and instructional coach in low-income high schools in San Antonio. Stephen's primary focus is the advancement of English learners and other disadvantaged students by promoting growth mindset and academic expression.

TINA BEENE is currently an Educational Consultant with Seidlitz Education. Her previous educational roles include: bilingual classroom teacher, bilingual program coordinator, and secondary ESL facilitator. She is the author of *Teaching Social Studies to ELLs* and has developed a variety of professional development sessions with a focus on engagement, language acquisition, and ELPS implementation.

SEIDLITZ EDUCATION BOOK ORDER FORM

   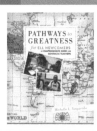  

TITLE	PRICE	QTY	TOTAL$
38 Great Academic Language Builders	$24.95		
7 Pasos para crear un aula interactiva y rica en lenguaje SPANISH	$29.95		
7 Steps to a Language-Rich Interactive Classroom	$29.95		
7 Steps To a Language-Rich, Interactive Foreign Language Classroom	$32.95		
Boosting Achievement: Reaching Students with Interrupted or Minimal Education	$26.95		
Content Review & Practice for the TX ESL 154	$39.95		
Content Review & Practice for the TX Bilingual 164	$39.95		
Content Review & Practice for the TX Spanish 190	$39.95		
Diverse Learner Flip Book	$26.95		
ELLs in Texas: What Teachers Need to Know 2ND ED.	$34.95		
ELs in Texas: What School Leaders Need to Know 3RD ED.	$34.95		
ELPS Flip Book	$19.95		
English/Spanish Linguistic and Academic Connections	$29.95		
Mi Cuaderno de Dictado SPANISH	$7.95		
Motivating ELLs: 27 Activities to Inspire & Engage Students	$26.95		
COLUMN 1 TOTAL $			

TITLE	PRICE	QTY	TOTAL$
Navigating the ELPS: Using the Standards to Improve Instruction for English Learners	$24.95		
Navigating the ELPS: Math 2ND EDITION	$29.95		
Navigating the ELPS: Science	$29.95		
Navigating the ELPS: Social Studies	$29.95		
Navigating the ELPS: Language Arts and Reading	$34.95		
Optimizando el desarrollo de la lectoescritura SPANISH	$39.95		
Pathways to Greatness for ELL Newcomers: A Comprehensive Guide for Schools & Teachers	$32.95		
Reading & Writing with English Learners	$29.95		
RTI for ELLs Fold-Out	$16.95		
Sheltered Instruction in Texas: Second Language Acquisition Methods for Teachers of ELs	$29.95		
Talk Read Talk Write: A Practical Routine for Learning in All Content Areas K-12 2ND ED.	$32.95		
Teaching Social Studies to ELLs	$24.95		
Teaching Science to English Learners	$24.95		
¡Toma la Palabra! SPANISH	$32.95		
Vocabulary Now! 44 Strategies All Teachers Can Use	$29.95		
COLUMN 2 TOTAL $			

Pricing, specifications, and availability subject to change without notice.

SHIPPING 9% of order total, minimum $14.95
5-7 business days to ship. If needed sooner please call for rates.
TAX EXEMPT? please fax a copy of your certificate along with order.

COLUMN 1+2	$
DISCOUNT	$
SHIPPING	$
TAX	$
TOTAL	$

HOW TO ORDER

PHONE (210) 315-7119 | **ONLINE** at **www.seidlitzeducation.com**

FAX completed form with payment info to **(949) 200-4384**

NAME

SHIPPING ADDRESS   CITY   STATE, ZIP

PHONE NUMBER   EMAIL ADDRESS

TO ORDER BY FAX
to **(949) 200-4384**
please complete
credit card info **or**
attach purchase order

☐ Visa ☐ MasterCard ☐ Discover ☐ AMEX

CARD #   EXPIRES
                                          mm/yyyy
SIGNATURE   CVV
                          3- or 4- digit code

☐ **Purchase Order attached**
please make
P.O. out to
Seidlitz Education

For information about Seidlitz Education products
and professional development, please contact us at

(210) 315-7119 | kathy@johnseidlitz.com
56 Via Regalo, San Clemente, CA 92673
www.seidlitzeducation.com

Giving kids the
gift of **academic
language.**™

REV062920

SEIDLITZ PRODUCT ORDER FORM

Three ways to order

- **FAX** completed order form with payment information to **(949) 200-4384**
- **PHONE** order information to **(210) 315-7119**
- **ORDER ONLINE** at **www.seidlitzeducation.com**

Pricing, specifications, and availability subject to change without notice.

TITLE	Price	QTY	TOTAL $
NEW! *Instead Of I Don't Know* Poster For the LOTE Classrrom 24" x 36"			
☐ LOTE FRENCH	$9.95		
☐ LOTE SPANISH	$9.95		
☐ LOTE GERMAN	$9.95		
	TOTAL $		

TITLE	Price	QTY	TOTAL $
Instead Of I Don't Know Poster, 24" x 36"			
☐ Elementary ENGLISH	$9.95		
☐ Secondary ENGLISH	$9.95		
20 pack *Instead Of I Don't Know* Posters, 11" x 17"			
☐ Elementary ENGLISH	$40.00		
☐ Secondary ENGLISH	$40.00		
Instead Of I Don't Know Poster, 24" x 36" Elementary SPANISH	$9.95		
20 pack *Instead Of I Don't Know* Posters, 11" x 17" Elementary SPANISH	$40.00		
	TOTAL $		

TITLE	Price	QTY	TOTAL $
Academic Language Cards and Activity Booklet, ENGLISH	$19.95		
Academic Language Cards, SPANISH	$9.95		
	TOTAL $		

TITLE	Price	QTY	TOTAL $
Please Speak In Complete Sentences Poster 24" x 36"			
☐ ENGLISH ☐ SPANISH	$9.95		
20 pack *Please Speak In Complete Sentences* Posters, 11" x 17"			
☐ ENGLISH ☐ SPANISH	$40.00		
	TOTAL $		

SHIPPING 9% of order total, minimum $14.95
5-7 business days to ship.
If needed sooner please call for rates.

TAX EXEMPT? please fax a copy of your certificate along with order.

GRAND TOTAL	$
DISCOUNT	$
SHIPPING	$
TAX	$
FINAL TOTAL	$

NAME _____

SHIPPING ADDRESS _____ CITY _____ STATE, ZIP _____

PHONE NUMBER _____ EMAIL ADDRESS _____

TO ORDER BY FAX
to **(949) 200-4384**
please complete
credit card info *or*
attach purchase order

☐ Visa ☐ MasterCard ☐ Discover ☐ AMEX

CARD # _____ EXPIRES _____ mm/yyyy

SIGNATURE _____ CVV _____

☐ **Purchase Order**

please make
P.O. out to
Seidlitz Education